PRAISE FOR ROSE REISMAN

"Rose Reisman's simplistic approach to living well makes you feel that you can achieve a new level of living without completely turning your life upside down. She's encouraging and wants us to understand the value of 'living well.'"
—Marilyn Denis, host of *CityLine*

"*The Balance of Living Well* offers practical approaches to achieving greater balance in the many aspects of our busy lives, with self-help guidelines to empower people to design their own lifestyle solutions."
—Ellie Tesher, advice columnist, *Toronto Star*

"Balance is a hot buzzword, but Rose Reisman has thought it through and applied it to more facets of contemporary life than anyone else. She's our diva of domesticity."
—Ellen Roseman, personal finance columnist, *Toronto Star*

"Dynamic businesswoman and devoted mom."
—*Edmonton Sun*

"Reisman's attitude is encouraging, without the fake and annoying hyper-enthusiasm that pervades the weight-loss and self-help book industry. She gives advice on combining food groups and savvy shopping. Her recipes successfully pique the interest—and the taste buds."
—*Toronto Star*

"Eating well is the best revenge. Rose Reisman's approach is sensible—the whole family can enjoy light dishes."
—*Toronto Star*

"Rose Reisman has a great formula for finding your perfect weight-loss path."
—*Canadian Living*

"With her menagerie consisting of a husband, four children, two dogs, two cats, plus teaching cooking classes, writing a newspaper column, and a busy schedule of appearances, one might wonder just how Rose Reisman finds time to create cookbooks. However, she does and *Weekday Wonders* is one of the delicious results of her tireless culinary efforts. She is also very active in the fight against breast cancer, and her books, *Weekday Wonders* included, are often used as fundraisers by the Canadian Breast Cancer Foundation. Good food for a good cause."

—Leslie Beck, RD

"The GenerX Corporation today announced that Touchstone on Lake Muskoka has been awarded the Rose Reisman Seal of Approval by acclaimed author and lifestyle advocate Rose Reisman. 'We are very fortunate indeed in attracting Rose Reisman's seal of approval,' says Walter Thompson, President of GenerX. 'As an author, consultant, and speaker she is an advocate for healthy lifestyles. A healthy and balanced lifestyle is an intrinsic part of what Touchstone represents.'"

—Walter Thomson, President, Touchstone Vacation Property, Lake Muskoka

"Rose Reisman has the knack of bringing to her cooking and cookbooks a light, healthy cuisine—yet they sparkle with great flavour points. Her approach to well-being through the use of simple, nutritious but easy-to-source ingredients proves that beautiful meals can still be realized without spending hours in the kitchen."

—Judy Creighton

"We truly appreciate Rose's continued commitment to the foundation as it helps us to continue our mission to make a difference in the lives of women, and men, touched by breast cancer."

—Lyn McDonell, Chief Executive Office, Canadian Breast Cancer Foundation

"Rose is like a coach. She explains what you can do to maintain a healthy weight for life and to enjoy increased energy. It's not complicated, but it does take courage and commitment. Here's an opportunity to take charge of your life and your health—one small step at a time. It's worth it."

—Dr. Marla Shapiro, CTV medical correspondent

"VON (Victorian Order of Nurses) Canada Foundation is pleased and honoured to be the recipient of the generous and overwhelming support of Rose Reisman. On behalf of our staff, volunteers, and clients, we applaud Rose for helping build healthy communities one person at a time."

—Jeff Beach, Executive Director, VON Canada

PENGUIN CANADA

the balance of living well

ROSE REISMAN is the bestselling author of fifteen books, a registered nutritional consultant, a partner in Rose Reisman Catering, a newspaper columnist, and a motivational speaker. She is a regular guest on national television and radio. She lives in Toronto with her husband and four children.

Also by Rose Reisman

Secrets for Permanent Weight Loss

Weekday Wonders

The Complete Idiot's Guide® to Light Desserts

The Art of Living Well

Divine Indulgences

Sensationally Light Pasta and Grains

Rose Reisman's Light Vegetarian Cooking

Rose Reisman's Enlightened Kitchen

Rose Reisman's Enlightened Home Cooking

Rose Reisman Brings Home Light Pasta

Rose Reisman Brings Home Light Cooking

Rose Reisman Brings Home Pasta Dishes

Rose Reisman Brings Home Spa Desserts

Manhattan's Dessert Scene

The Dessert Scene

rose reisman

the balance of living well

6 ways to achieve
total harmony in your life

PENGUIN
CANADA

PENGUIN CANADA

Published by the Penguin Group

Penguin Group (Canada), 90 Eglinton Avenue East, Suite 700, Toronto, Ontario, Canada M4P 2Y3
(a division of Pearson Canada Inc.)

Penguin Group (USA) Inc., 375 Hudson Street, New York, New York 10014, U.S.A.
Penguin Books Ltd, 80 Strand, London WC2R 0RL, England
Penguin Ireland, 25 St Stephen's Green, Dublin 2, Ireland (a division of Penguin Books Ltd)
Penguin Group (Australia), 250 Camberwell Road, Camberwell, Victoria 3124, Australia
(a division of Pearson Australia Group Pty Ltd)
Penguin Books India Pvt Ltd, 11 Community Centre, Panchsheel Park, New Delhi – 110 017, India
Penguin Group (NZ), cnr Airborne and Rosedale Roads, Albany, Auckland 1310, New Zealand
(a division of Pearson New Zealand Ltd)
Penguin Books (South Africa) (Pty) Ltd, 24 Sturdee Avenue, Rosebank, Johannesburg 2196, South Africa

Penguin Books Ltd, Registered Offices: 80 Strand, London WC2R 0RL, England

First published 2006

(QUE) 10 9 8 7 6 5 4 3 2 1

Copyright © Rose Reisman, 2006
Interior photos: Image Source/Brand X Pictures/Banana Stock/ThinkStock Images
Contents photograph (page viii): Lorella Zanetti
Wheel of Life illustration (page 6): David Cheung
Interior design: Soapbox Design

Manufactured in Canada.

LIBRARY AND ARCHIVES CANADA CATALOGUING IN PUBLICATION

Reisman, Rose, 1953–
    The balance of living well : 6 ways to achieve total harmony in your life / Rose Reisman.

ISBN-13: 978-0-14-305152-7
ISBN-10: 0-14-305152-0

1. Self-actualization (Psychology). 2. Life skills. I. Title.

BF637.S4R46 2006   158.1   C2006-902453-7

Visit the Penguin Group (Canada) website at **www.penguin.ca**

Special and corporate bulk purchase rates available; please see **www.penguin.ca/corporatesales**
or call 1-800-399-6858, ext. 477 or 474

dedication

My incredible family is what keeps my life in balance. They keep me focused and remind me of what's important in life.

Sam, I can't believe we've made it 30 years! I seem to love you more each year. You are my inspiration, and together we make a great team.

Natalie, may you continue to "inhale" life as you do each day. There are just not enough hours in a day for you.

David, you bring peace to your family, friends, and every situation you find yourself in. The glass is always half full.

Laura, you have become a confident young woman with a passionate heart. Mount Holyoke will bring out your full potential.

Adam, only fourteen and you have surpassed my expectations. The warmth of your smile melts me each day. Stay always so sweet.

My four "furry" friends bring me a sense of calm throughout my day. My two German Shepherds, Aspen and Meiko, and my two Ragdoll cats, Misty and Ozzie.

contents

Acknowledgments

When I began this book, I was looking to respond to people's request for insight on how to lead a balanced life. Thanks to the team at Penguin Canada, including Tracy Bordian, Andrea Crozier, Ed Carson, David Davidar, Elizabeth McKay, and Judy Phillips, for their commitment to each book we've worked on together. They're an incredibly professional team to work with and you can't imagine how much I appreciate it. They make my job so easy. A special thanks to Karen Basian, Elfreda Chang, and Leslie Bontje for sifting through my stories (and my closets), to find the insights and tools that make my life work (and often the words to describe them). It was their determination that allowed me to examine what I do and how I do it that breathed life and brought much depth to many of the chapters. My thanks to them, their faith and belief that what I had to say was important and should be told. A special thank you to Howard Gold, my agent, who has cheered me on despite many an anxious moment, and who does not stop expecting only the greatest things. It's hard to admit, but his directness is always appreciated.

As always, to my incredible family, who allow me to do what I love each day. Sam, my soulmate for 30 years. There are no words to describe the love, admiration, and respect I have for him and his unconditional love for me. My four unique and such special children, Natalie, David, Laura, and Adam. They have turned out to be such amazing people. My family keeps me positive and allows my life to continue moving with such force.

Rose Reisman

VON

CANADA

Touching Lives Since 1897
Au coeur de la vie depuis

Dear Reader,

VON (Victorian Order of Nurses) Canada Foundation is pleased and honoured to be the recipient of the generous and overwhelming support of Rose Reisman.

By purchasing this book you are helping to build healthier communities, not only by improving your own health, but also by supporting VON's much-needed home care and community charitable programs like Meals on Wheels, Volunteer Visiting, and healthy breakfast programs for kids in schools.

For more than 100 years, VON has served as Canada's leading national, not-for-profit, charitable, home care and community support organization. VON touches the lives of over 1 million people every year through more than 50 programs in 1,400 Canadian communities.

On behalf of our staff, volunteers, and clients, we applaud Rose for helping build healthy communities one person at a time.

With thanks,

Donald W. Storch
Chair
VON Canada Foundation

Jeffrey D. Beach
Executive Director
VON Canada Foundation

balanced
living

my recipe for the wheel of life

Over the course of my career, I have met many people from all walks of life. As you might expect, because I've written fifteen books, I'm asked lots of questions, several of them about healthy approaches to cooking and eating—how to decrease the fat or sugar in a recipe, or what's in my pantry. But I continue to be surprised that the bulk of questions I'm asked have nothing at all to do with food. Instead, they are about family and marriage, home life versus career, coping with teenagers, and finding time to stay fit and eat healthy. I'm also often asked what motivates me, and how I manage to feel and look young (that last one flatters the heck out of me). I think that, when all these questions are boiled down to their essence, what people are asking me for is my recipe for life—how I juggle it all—how I fit it all in.

And I wondered, what makes my recipe different? What is the secret of my success, if I have one? Do I have a life philosophy that helps me manage the competing demands of my life? So, to my readers and devotees, I thank you for inspiring me to try to distill and then assemble it all, and then to clearly articulate my approach, here in this book.

The world is full of different and individual people. But, what I see, over and over again, is that the challenges we face are not unique. My hope is that my ideas and the techniques that I

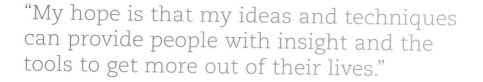

"My hope is that my ideas and techniques can provide people with insight and the tools to get more out of their lives."

present here can provide my readers with insight and the tools to get more out of their lives. We all want more out of life than just healthy and strong bodies. If that were all we cared about, we'd eat only healthy foods, spend inordinate amounts of time at the gym, and none of us would experience anxiety at the beginning of swimsuit season. But, that's not the reality of the lives we lead, nor the priorities we set. We have seemingly endless demands on our time. Much as we may get tired of it, multi-tasking looks like it's here to stay. We never have enough time in the day to fit all our obligations, let alone discretionary activities, into the picture.

I began explaining my idea for creating a healthy life in *The Art of Living Well*. In this book, *The Balance of Living Well*, I have tried to paint the whole picture as well as the underlying methodology to living a better quality of life. I had started out on my journey toward overall wellness by learning how to make the body healthy—I examined what we put into our bodies to fuel them and how we exercise our bodies to make them strong. Since, as I said, we all want more out of life than just healthy bodies, once I understood wellness in relationship to

food and exercise, I was interested to see how my philosophy of health could be applied to other areas of my life. But before I explain what I discovered, let me tell you a bit about what brought me to this point.

My Health History

When I was in my early thirties, I learned the hard way that how you feel is not always an accurate indicator of how well you are. At the time, I was at a healthy weight and I thought I looked pretty fit. I exercised every single day. I had lots of energy, and I was excited that my new career as a cookbook author was going well—my latest book, containing deliciously decadent high-fat desserts, was heading for bestseller status. Then I went to my doctor for my annual physical and learned that my cholesterol level was through the roof. Every day for months before the publication of my book I had been taste-testing desserts made from my recipes—not exactly a healthy diet. I knew that my family history included heart disease and stroke, as well as diabetes. My grandmother was diabetic, my mother obese, and my father had died of a massive heart attack when I was sixteen and he was only fifty-seven. His sister died exactly the same way a few months later. My uncle, my father's brother, had symptoms of heart disease. He immediately started on a program of sensible eating and exercise and ended up living a healthy life until the age of eighty-six.

It just didn't seem fair that I had a serious health problem at such a young age, especially when I exercised every day. But, as we all know, in life you have to play the hand you're dealt—genetic or otherwise. I knew I was going to have to follow my uncle's example and fight back against my family's health history if I wanted to be well.

That's when I began to read and learn everything I could about health, wellness, and finding life balance. I've since written several articles and bestselling books about wellness and cooking as I've gathered information. It's been a journey that I've enjoyed and from which my entire family has benefited. They all eat healthier meals now and know more about nutrition because of the balanced food I prepare for them. I believe that this knowledge will help them live long, healthy lives. And since my husband and I have adopted active lifestyles, our children have learned from our example and done the same. My work in this direction has meant that each member of my family has designed his or her own version of health in balance.

Balance: Health and Wellness

What has become clear to me through all this is that achieving the goal of living well is about designing a method to continually improve the various elements of my life, and then developing an ongoing working balance between all these essential but competing parts. That means finding a way to combine having a healthy body and mind, a healthy—and fun—emotional life with family and friends, and a healthy financial life, one that includes a rewarding career. But continually working to improve each of these areas of my life, and at the same time maintaining a balance between them, is not easy.

It seems that so many of us are engaged in the same struggle to achieve balance between the competing parts of our lives. We feel we are spread too thin and in all directions. We want to be good and loving partners. We want to nurture, cherish, and build confidence in our children. We want to enjoy the company of good friends. We want to enjoy good food and wine, the arts, our hobbies. We want to be well read and well informed. We want to look good and age well. We want to be successful at our careers and be financially secure. Let's face it. We want to work hard and have fun too. And these are all worthwhile and understandable goals.

Having It All

Are we expecting too much from our lives? Do we indeed have to settle for doing and achieving less, sacrificing one part of our lives so that a goal in another part is achieved? Is having it all an impossible dream? The answer isn't yes, but it's not a simple no, either.

It seems to me that the messages contained in the books and articles I've read on the subject fall into two categories. Many suggest I have the right, maybe even the obligation, to be a superwoman—to have it all; that it's just a matter of increasing my efficiency. Others point out that if I am unable to fulfill my potential as a superwoman, it is someone else's fault. Some articles combine these two theories. I don't find any of these approaches very encouraging, since a) I am going flat-out most of the time and I still have trouble fitting in all I want to do, b) I tend not to blame others for how my life is going and, c) I do like to feel I have control over the direction and outcome of my life.

After much thought and plenty of trial and error, I arrived at my answer, which is that we *can* have it all—*just not all at once*. It's unrealistic and overwhelming to try to achieve your objective of an ideal life overnight, or even in a week or two—it is the small steps that are going to get you there. Life will never be perfectly balanced but you can reach a better balance over time. I think this answer is purely pragmatic, and I'm a big fan of pragmatism. I don't think you succeed in designing the life you want by getting hung-up on idealism that doesn't work in practice.

So, where does one begin? How does one go about designing this ideal life? I believe you start by recognizing that life does not stand still. It is always changing and evolving—it's dynamic. This means that the system has to accommodate ever-shifting priorities and objectives.

Get Organized: The Six Fs

The next step is to get organized. You can't begin this process until you break down your personal hodgepodge of demands, obligations, priorities, and options into smaller pieces than just "life in general." So, my method begins by defining and dividing my life into its various components— into the distinct areas I feel have importance and that I put energy into. Most people I meet have similar parts to their lives. Mine are **Fitness, Food, Family, Friends, Fashion,** and **Finance**—I call them my six Fs, and together they make up my wheel of life. You will have your own life sections, influenced by your own choices and interests. The system I outline in this book will work well for whatever your life looks like.

Next, you need to look carefully at each life area, one at a time, assessing where you are now and then defining where you want to be, what your ideal situation looks like. These are not steps to rush through. It sometimes takes time and courage to look honestly and objectively at your life, determining what would really make you happy. This last step requires that you take the time to know what you want—not what someone else wants, or worse, what someone else thinks you should want. If the contrast

Wheel of Life

Family

Fitness

Friends

Food

Fashion

Finance

between where you are and where you want to be is stark, don't let that slow you down. I'll show you in this book how to tackle it. You'll have to be prepared to periodically revisit and re-evaluate where you are and where you want to be, because these points will likely change at various times in your life.

Let's use the example of family. You could ask yourself, am I the kind of partner I want to be? Does my partner feel that I'm carrying my share of the load, and vice versa? Do I spend the amount of time I want to with my children? Am I providing the kind of support for my children that they need? Take time to reflect on these questions before answering. Once you have a

good understanding of how things are at the moment, visualize how you want them to look. Don't be afraid to think creatively, because you're the only one who can determine what will work for you. And if there's one thing I've learned, it's that if something in your life is bothering you, it's important to be proactive. No one's life ever improved by just wishing and wanting.

Once you have the answers to the questions about where you are and where you want to be, you're ready to face the hardest and most important part: taking the first step toward change.

Start by Focusing on One Thing

I use my husband's philosophy for tackling change in my life. He always says, "Just do one thing right." He applies this philosophy to everything he undertakes. What he means is that you need to prioritize. Figure out what the most important thing to do is, then do it right. You're then ready to move on to the next priority. Don't get bogged down with the enormity of the project. Break each task into bite-sized pieces that you can focus on until each is completed. That way you do a good job on each of the segments, giving you quality building blocks that can be put together to form a solid and strong structure.

The idea of starting with just "one thing" is very appealing to me. It makes change manageable and doable rather than intimidating. What I do is prioritize the one thing I can do each day that will most improve my life. I focus on it and complete it to the best of my ability. Naturally, the task can take more than one day to complete, but I persevere until it's done, and done properly. After completing each "one thing," I am able to go on to the next.

This approach has several advantages. I don't have unrealistic expectations about what I will get done in a day. I budget enough time and energy to make sure I can do my "one thing" right. And I pat myself on the back when I complete each of these bite-sized benchmarks. Sure I make plenty of mistakes, but I learn from them and just keep working away on my "one thing," one thing at a time.

When I have completed each job "right," I have completed a quality building block, which I can add to a growing foundation. The foundation, in turn, forms the base of the solid and strong structure of my life.

I also find that focusing on one thing or task helps make change easier to integrate into my life. Usually, adding one thing at a time to your life does not represent a change that's too big or too radical to absorb. I hate to admit it, but, like most people, I resist change, sometimes without even realizing it. "One thing" at a time feels gradual—they're small steps. I like that. And yet, when I've added quite a few small changes to my life over time and then pause to look back, I'm sometimes astounded at the transformation I have achieved.

The next part of the process involves creating an ongoing balance between the various work-in-progress elements of my life. Here again the idea of doing One Thing Right at a time proves invaluable. Because I make only one thing top priority, I rarely feel overwhelmed. And by constantly evaluating which priority is the most important to me at any given moment, I make sure that what I *want* to do doesn't consistently take a backseat to what I have to do.

So, by now I've probably created the impression that I believe I have a perfectly balanced, ideal life—that I manage all obstacles in my path with effortless serenity; that my marriage and my children are also perfect. In other words, you've pretty much decided I'm some kind of smile-in-the-face-of-all-conflict superwoman or that I'm living a life of complete denial. Thank goodness, neither is true.

The Juggling Act

I'm far from perfect, and my life isn't perfect either. And I sometimes have trouble keeping all my balls in the air. But I look at balance as a dynamic process. It's an equilibrium, which in a dynamic world means that it will constantly be challenged and requires constant adjustment to maintain. I find it easiest and most successful to focus on making adjustments one at a time, otherwise I would need to introduce too many balls at once. I prefer to take my cue from jugglers, who establish a rhythm with their first two or three balls before introducing another ball, then integrating that ball into their juggling rhythm before adding yet another.

The other thing I try to remember is that balance doesn't mean I'm unemotional about life's ups and downs. When things aren't going well in my relationship with my husband or with my children, with a client or with a friend, I can get really upset. Some of us may find it difficult to control our emotions—it is much easier to control our actions. While I can feel down about an issue, I don't let myself wallow too long in negative emotion before I kick into

action. As with most of us, my problems aren't all simple and easily fixable; doing One Thing Right might be tough, involving substantial effort over a long period. I just do my best to persevere and I ask for help if I need it. Keeping my "one thing" small enough makes even the most difficult parts of my life manageable.

Thank goodness all life's day-to-day issues aren't huge challenges. Much of what we encounter, what's taking up big chunks of our time and clogging up the works, are small irritating inefficiencies, little fires that need to be put out. Usually it's merely the sheer volume of minor matters that's causing the backlog. Working to eliminate procrastination by chipping away at your problems, one thing at a time, can do a lot to simplify your life. And the fact is, occasionally making a problem go away can be as simple as having a good cry or getting a good night's sleep. Every life is an ongoing journey, but if you have a system for coping with the potholes in the road, whether small or crater-like, and even for changing the direction you are travelling in, life's a lot easier.

Giving Ourselves a Break

This leads me back full circle to my point about the many questions I receive—and the misconceptions I hear about balance. I am continually amazed at how hard people can be on themselves. Many perfectly rational people believe that achieving balance in their lives means doing everything to the max, perfectly, every time, every day. And what a surprise: Putting that kind of pressure of perfection on themselves is making them crazy. And having raised the bar so high, it's no wonder that people despair of ever reaching any kind of sustainable equilibrium.

That's why I believe a book like this one is necessary. For me, balance is not about perfection. I give myself a lot more of a break than that. As long as I'm making some progress every day—a few small steps' worth—I am happy. I believe that a significant part of my success—what makes my system work, and what makes my objectives attainable—is due to the way I define balance: as being in charge of my priorities, giving weight to what really matters to me, and working at my life improvements "one thing" at a time. As I said before, I believe we can have it all, just not all at once.

This relaxed and realistic approach works for me because it allows me to address the issues we all face in a proactive and empowering manner. It gives me the tools I need to ensure that all the areas of my life get time and attention. In other words, it allows me to attain what eludes so many of us: balance.

My definition of balance means that I am able to balance each one of my six Fs against the others. I don't sacrifice my family or my friendships for my career. I make time to take care of my health. I don't fall into the trap of feeling selfish because I do some things just for me.

Your Own Balance

Just as I create my own framework for balance, so will each of you. Each of us has a different understanding of what balance means because each of us has her or his own owner's manual. The key is to identify the core elements that need to be part of your equation and to then structure these to create your individual balance.

Built into my philosophy of a healthy and balanced life are trade-offs and compromises, mechanisms for improvement and change. There are realistic goals and expectations. There is moderation. And my life works for me. Balance works. Use this book as a guide on your own personal journey in defining your priorities and life segments, and in finding your own path to the balance of your life.

fitness
feeling
my
best

fitness feeling my best

How do you feel? Do you feel strong, energetic, alert, and ready to go every morning? The key to being able to answer yes to this last question lies in being active every day (and in eating healthy, the topic of Chapter 2). When you move, your heart rate increases and your blood oxygenates. As a result, oxygen and nutrients flow more readily through your body to fuel your cells. When you move consistently and for at least 30 minutes at a time, you increase your strength and endurance, boost your immune system, and improve your mood.

Most of us have some improvement to make to our fitness. It's okay to admit things aren't terrific in this area. But you do deserve to feel healthy and energized every day. Even if you are having trouble getting rid of extra weight, are out of breath walking up a flight of stairs or running to the car, feeling tired all the time, or getting sick a lot, you don't have to work out like a professional athlete to get significant benefits.

You can start by making small changes involving a little movement every day. Small steps over time will get you to where you want to be. The fitness segment of your wheel of life is important to keep the other areas in balance. When you feel fit, you'll eat better, have more energy for your family and friends, look better, and in general be in better health.

"When you feel fit, you'll eat better, have more energy, look better, and be in better health."

Benefits of Regular Exercise

Aside from making you feel better in the short term, regular exercise has a number of long-term benefits.

Burns Calories and Reduces the Risk of Obesity
When you exercise regularly, some of your body fat will be replaced by muscle. Even at rest, muscle tissue burns up many more calories per day than fat does. So the more lean muscle mass you have, the more efficiently you'll burn calories. These are important points to keep in mind if one of your objectives in keeping fit is to lose weight. Studies show that the chances of succeeding at losing weight and keeping it off improve with increased muscle tissue from regular exercise and a balanced diet.

Decreases Your Risk of Heart Disease and Stroke Regular exercise, along with a diet low in saturated fat, is thought to dramatically lower your chance of developing heart disease or suffering a stroke.

Regulates Blood Pressure Increased physical activity, combined with a low-sodium and low-fat diet, can be instrumental in regulating blood pressure, thereby greatly reducing your risk of heart disease and stroke.

Improves Colon Health Regular exercise and a diet high in both fibre and water intake greatly improve bowel function. And, if combined with a diet low in saturated fat, it can reduce your risk of colon cancer.

Reduces the Risk of Certain Cancers According to cancer organizations, up to 70 percent of all cancers could be prevented if people made changes to their lifestyle. Approximately 20 to 33 percent of all cancers are related to what you eat. Evidence indicates that exercise may reduce the risk of or even prevent cancer of the colon and breast.

Prevents Type 2 Diabetes By maintaining a healthy body weight with regular exercise and a healthy diet, you can boost organ function and keep your weight within a healthy range, thereby significantly decreasing your chance of developing type 2 diabetes.

Offsets Alzheimer's Disease The increased flow of highly oxygenated blood to your brain from regular physical activity is believed to be an important factor in delaying or preventing Alzheimer's disease.

Wards Off Viral and Infectious Diseases
Exercise boosts your immune system, helping you ward off viral and infectious diseases of all kinds—from the common cold to some very serious strains of flu.

Increases Bone Density Engaging in weight-bearing exercise can increase bone density, which substantially decreases the risk of developing osteoporosis and osteoarthritis.

Keeps Depression at Bay People who lead an active life are less likely to suffer from insomnia or depression. Exercise is also often recommended for stress management. The release of endorphins through exercise—it's the endorphins that cause the high experienced after vigorous exercise—helps fight mood swings, anxiety, and stress, all of which can trigger poor eating habits, such as overeating or indulging in high-fat comfort food.

Makes You Look Younger and Increases Your Self-Esteem You can slow down the aging process of your skin by moving and breathing. Increased blood flow to your epidermis, which occurs during periods of exercise, supplies skin with oxygen and the nutrients it needs to maintain elasticity and a healthy glow. And looking and feeling younger will boost your self-esteem.

Makes You a Role Model for Your Family Set the right example for your family and friends by exercising and following a balanced diet.

Almost everyone I know wants to improve their physical health. Along with eating right, regular exercise is essential to achieving that goal. Yet, more broken New Year's resolutions seem to be about getting in shape than about anything else. Maintaining a consistent, long-term exercise program is the one thing we have trouble finding the time and energy for—maybe because it represents such a big change in our lives. And we all know that change can be tough. Once you are committed to making a change to your fitness, you'll need to implement a program—to find a fitness solution.

Essential Elements of an Exercise Program
To reap major benefits from exercise, including maintaining a healthy body weight, you'll need at least 3 to 5 hours of vigorous exercise each week. That's a minimum of approximately 30 minutes per day, or 50 minutes every other day. Getting active has never been more appealing. Fitness has changed over the years, becoming much more exciting and participatory, and many health clubs and gyms now offer innovative classes, such as spinning and kick-boxing, along with the latest sports equipment. You can read, listen to music, or even watch your own personal television while you work out.

A well-rounded exercise program consists of three essential elements: aerobic/cardiovascular training, muscle strengthening with weights, and flexibility/stretching work.

An aerobic/cardio program should last at least 20 minutes per session—the amount of time it usually takes to benefit from exercise once your optimum exercise heart rate has been reached. Cardiovascular exercise, which includes running, brisk walking, swimming, cycling, working out on cardio equipment, and aerobic classes, strengthens your heart, increases your lung capacity, and improves endurance.

Strength training develops muscle definition and increases your metabolic rate, the rate at which your body uses up its energy. It also reduces the risk of osteoporosis and helps you lose body fat. The traditional method of weight training is to perform multiple sets of each exercise to build muscle. It's now thought that the most effective way is to do a single set of each exercise with ten to fifteen repetitions or work to fatigue. Choosing a heavier weight and doing only one set of, say, twelve repetitions will give you the same results and save you time. When the exercise gets easy, it's time to increase the weight. A strengthening program might include working out with free weights or on weight equipment, Pilates or yoga, fitness- or medicine-ball exercises, and core-strengthening exercises. Do strengthening work on alternate days, replacing aerobic if necessary. It is ideal, though, to add strengthening exercises on top of your aerobic workout at least twice a week.

Flexibility and stretching exercises improve the range of motion in your joints (helping posture and mobility), help to prevent injuries during exercise, and prevent stiffness, both after exercising and in general. Pilates, yoga, tai chi, and a variety of stretch classes for various parts of the body offer good flexibility and stretching workouts. Stretch for 5 to 10 minutes per workout session.

Here's a list of common activities and the calories they burn. You may find it useful to refer to this chart as you design your fitness program.

"Almost everyone I know wants to improve their physical health. Along with eating right, regular exercise is essential to achieving that goal."

Calorie Expenditure (calories expended per hour)

BODY WEIGHT	125 LB	180 LB	BODY WEIGHT	125 LB	180 LB
Sport Activities			Snow shovelling	337	472
Aerobic classes	350	472	Spinning	400	556
Canoeing	340	472	Stair climbing	510	714
Cross-country skiing	457	640	Swimming—moderate	250	336
Cycling—moderate	367	529	Tennis—singles	450	640
Dancing—vigorous	285	400	Tennis—doubles	285	400
Downhill skiing	367	514	Walking—brisk	440	560
Elliptical trainer	550	750	Walking—moderate	247	350
Gardening	270	378	Weightlifting	245	385
Golfing (no cart)	217	304	Yoga	225	315
Hiking	400	546	**Home Activities**		
Hockey	400	546	Dusting	130	180
Horseback riding	240	336	Housecleaning	202	240
Jogging—moderate	562	810	Laundry	120	170
Karate	367	514	Making beds	120	170
Kick-boxing	460	600	Raking leaves	285	350
Rollerblading	397	556	Scrubbing floors	315	400
Skating	345	483	Vacuuming	140	190

SOURCE: WWW.CALORIECONTROL.ORG

Determining a Healthy Body Weight

Before embarking on an exercise program, it is a good idea to assess where you are at now in terms of fitness. And to properly assess your fitness level, you'll first need to determine your healthy body weight, and what your current weight actually means. Here are a few tools to help you do this.

Body Mass Index (BMI)

One of the most widely used methods of determining if you are at a healthy weight is the body mass index, or BMI. This standard method evaluates body weight in relation to height. The BMI is just one way to determine if you are an ideal weight, or are overweight or obese. It is not intended to be used for those under eighteen or those over sixty-five years of age, pregnant or lactating women, and highly muscular persons.

To calculate your body mass, multiply your weight in pounds by 705, and divide that number by your height in inches squared. For example, if a woman weighs 150 pounds and her height is 5 feet 6 inches (66 inches):

$$150 \text{ lb} \times 705 = 105{,}750$$

Next, calculate the height in inches squared, by multiplying the number by itself:

$$66 \times 66 = 4356$$

Now divide the first total by the second total:

$$105{,}750 \div 4356 = 24.28$$

So, in this instance, the woman's BMI is 24.28.

Understanding Your BMI

BMI	WEIGHT STATUS
Below 18.5	Underweight
18.5–24.9	Normal
25.0–29.9	Overweight
30 and higher	Obese

People who are overweight or obese are at increased risk of high blood pressure, high blood cholesterol, and diabetes. These conditions increase the risk of heart disease and stroke.

Waist-to-Hip Ratio

The latest research indicates that the BMI has some shortcomings when determining a person's health risks. Abdominal fat, which involves the waist-to-hip ratio and waist circumference measurement, tends to be a better indicator. It's not just how much fat you have that matters: Where the fat is on your body is also important. In terms of weight distribution, people can be described as apples or pears. Women typically collect fat in their hips and buttocks, giving them a pear shape. Men generally collect weight around their bellies, giving them more of an apple shape. People with fat concentrated around the abdomen—those who are apple shaped—are more likely to develop many of the health problems associated with obesity.

To find out what shape you are, calculate your waist-to-hip ratio by dividing your waist measurement by your hip measurement.

Women with a waist-to-hip ratio of more than 0.8 or men with a ratio of more than 1.0 are apples, and their fat distribution is a health risk.

Body Fat Measurements

Sports instructors, registered dietitians, and doctors often measure body fat with callipers, pinching the fat in certain areas of the body to determine total body fat percentage. Men with more than 25 percent body fat and women with more than 30 percent body fat are considered obese.

Regular exercise helps to burn calories; reduce the risk of obesity, heart disease, certain cancers, and type 2 diabetes; and increase bone density.

where am I now?

Where do you feel your physical health is today? Do you have lots of energy to get everything done in your day that you want to? Or do you run out of fuel by the late afternoon?

The following questions will help you determine your current physical state. We'll start with the original question about how you feel:

Do I feel strong, energized, alert, and ready to go every morning when I wake up?

☐ Yes ☐ No

Do I exercise at least 3 times per week, with my heart rate elevated for at least 20 minutes each time?

☐ Yes ☐ No

Am I at a comfortable and healthy weight for me?

☐ Yes ☐ No

What conditions are found in my family history?—

Alzheimer's disease	☐ Yes	☐ No
Cancer	☐ Yes	☐ No
Diabetes/hypoglycemia (insulin/sugar-based sensitivity)	☐ Yes	☐ No
Heart disease	☐ Yes	☐ No
High blood pressure	☐ Yes	☐ No
Obesity	☐ Yes	☐ No
Osteoporosis or osteoarthritis	☐ Yes	☐ No
Stroke	☐ Yes	☐ No

If you answered no to any of the first three questions, it might be a good idea to start moving. If you have a predisposition to any of the genetic diseases listed, you have even more reason to exercise regularly—exercise will help reduce your risk of these diseases.

The last question to consider is: Even if I *feel* well, do I know for sure that I *am* well? Having a complete physical examination by your doctor is the only way to really know how you are doing health-wise. Combined with the answers to the above questions, the results of your physical will tell you exactly where you are now. The exam should determine your resting and active heart rate, blood pressure, cholesterol, fat percentage, and BMI. It also should include a stress test, which shows how your heart performs during exercise, and an electrocardiogram, which shows how your heart beats at rest. As well, a physical will reveal any health reason you may have for *not* exercising.

Once you've been to your doctor for a physical and are armed with the results, you're ready to move to the next phase of implementing change: Determining where you want to be in terms of physical fitness.

where do I want to be?

So, where do you want to be? Envision a healthy and fit you. What does that feel and look like? The following questions and suggestions will help you design a fitness program that will get you to where you want to be. They factor in your current fitness level and genetic history, as well as your lifestyle, interests, budget, and time constraints.

Physical examination completed on (date):

_____

Results of physical:

Cholesterol reading

Below normal ☐   Normal ☐   Above normal ☐

Blood pressure

Below normal ☐   Normal ☐   Above normal ☐

Weight

Below normal ☐   Normal ☐   Above normal ☐

Stress test (electrocardiogram)

Below normal ☐   Normal ☐   Above normal ☐

Doctor's recommendations:

_____

_____

_____

What is my ideal healthy weight? _____

What kinds of activities do I like to do?
Yoga, dance lessons, tennis, golf, jogging,
walking, swimming, cycling, weight training?
(Be open to whatever interests you.)

_____

_____

_____

What will it cost in equipment or club
memberships to pursue my favourite sports
and activities?

_____

_____

_____

Can I afford it?   ☐ Yes   ☐ No

If no, what alternatives will I enjoy that are less
expensive?

_____

_____

_____

Do I want or need someone to pursue this
activity with me (e.g., a partner for doubles
tennis)?   ☐ Yes   ☐ No

If yes, two people I want to join me in this
activity are:

Name: _____

Name: _____

If no, what are two options that I can do on my
own?

1. _____

2. _____

Do I need variety to keep from getting bored or do I like the routine of doing the same exercise every day?

Variety ☐   Routine ☐

How often do I have time to exercise? (Aim for 3 to 5 times a week.) _____

Which days? _____

If I travel for my work, can I find the time and place to work out?   ☐ Yes   ☐ No

If no, what physical activities will I do when I'm away for more than 2 days?

_____

_____

_____

What time of day works best for me to exercise?

Early morning ☐   Lunch ☐
After work ☐   Evening ☐

Do I have a genetic predisposition to any diseases that indicate I should pursue certain kinds of preventative exercise (e.g., osteoporosis, osteoarthritis—weight-bearing exercise; back problems—yoga, Pilates, or core-strengthening; heart disease, stroke, diabetes, cancer, Alzheimer's disease, weight loss—cardiovascular exercises to elevate the heart rate)?

☐ Yes   ☐ No

If yes, what are they?

_____

_____

_____

_____

_____

_____

_____

_____

_____

_____

_____

Take a close look at your answers. They will give you a good idea of what sorts of exercise you might pursue and how often. Write down your specific short- and long-term goals before you start an exercise program. Simply saying that you want to start jogging, cycling, or swimming is too vague. State how often you realistically can do the exercise, the time of day, the length of time, and what you want to achieve. The Fitness Goals chart opposite will help you get started.

Fitness Goals

SHORT-TERM GOALS

EXERCISE	FREQUENCY	TIME OF DAY	DURATION	DESIRED RESULT
e.g., walking	3 times/week	7 a.m.	30 min.	increase to 5 times/week

LONG-TERM GOALS

EXERCISE	FREQUENCY	TIME OF DAY	DURATION	DESIRED RESULT
e.g., jogging	4 times/week	6:30 a.m.	30 min.	lose weight/tone muscles

Once you have designed your fitness program, either on your own or with the help of a professional athletic trainer, it is sure to be one that really suits you and that you will enjoy. Let yourself get excited about the possibilities for your health. Then, block off on your calendar the times that you have decided will work for you and get started!

Do One Thing Right

One secret to success that I have learned is what I call the One Thing Right rule. If you want to succeed, try to make a change in only one area of your life at a time. I've seen people fail so often because they've tried to do too much at once. They are the people who decide they're going to get organized by cleaning out their cupboards and closets, lose weight by starting a diet and exercising, and save money by implementing a savings program—all on the same day. They've made the job so big and so daunting that they soon feel completely overwhelmed and give up.

I believe in taking my cue from jugglers. Jugglers start out by tossing one ball, and they don't add a second ball until they've established a confident rhythm with the first. The third ball isn't added until the first two are moving in a regular pattern.

The point is that, whatever change you undertake, start with small steps—because being the tortoise instead of the hare is the way to win the race. As a cook, I can tell you that it pays to add ingredients slowly and in small increments. If you add a lot of salt quickly to a recipe without stopping to check the taste, you can easily ruin a dish. I can also tell you that, just as with cooking, trial and error is often the only way to get it right. I've thrown out a lot of food along the way and had to start over. Making mistakes is an important part of making progress. The same is true of implementing change in your life balance. While developing your fitness solution requires consistent effort in spite of the setbacks, you will find that it can be the kindest and most empowering thing you ever do for yourself. And you will find that the benefits spill over into every other element of your life.

Your Fitness Affects Everything

I'll give you some examples of how fitness has affected other areas of my life. For years, early every morning, I have walked or hiked with my dogs to a nearby ravine. My eldest daughter, who is a young adult, asked me if I enjoy it. I told her how peaceful and beautiful I find my early morning walks. One day during her summer holidays, she asked to join me. She too enjoyed the walk, and it became something we regularly do together when she's at home. So in addition to bringing me closer to my husband, who is my weekend walking companion, dog walking has been good for my relationship with my daughter. Not only do we both feel fit together but something as simple as a walk has been another way to connect.

A new fitness routine with a focus on weight training that I have recently introduced to my workout week has made me feel stronger, as well as helped my metabolism operate more efficiently. I've learned how to ensure my form and technique are correct so that I optimize my weight-training efforts. Not only have I seen great results in body definition since I started on this program but I am now able to do things I didn't have enough endurance or strength to do before, which is empowering. Let me give you another example. On a family trip to the Rockies last summer, we heli-hiked: A helicopter dropped us off on one mountain, and we hiked from there to another, where we were picked up. The hike is about 2 hours. My family was impressed that I led the group, and it proved to me that one's age has little to do with one's fitness level.

The time you choose to work out must best serve your schedule. I work out every morning before my day starts. I vary my exercise so I won't get bored and lose motivation. Even though eating healthy food has been a focus of mine for years, my workouts keep me on track in terms of balancing my input and output. I don't want to undo all the good I've done in my morning workout (which I do before dropping the kids off at school and walking the dogs) by eating a large muffin or Danish pastry at my local coffee shop. I need the motivation my workouts give me to stay disciplined about what I eat. And it is a constant challenge because my work focuses on food all day long. Consciously not overeating—beating the urge to constantly nibble on the food that's in front of me—makes me proud of myself and of my own wellness. (The recipes you'll find starting on page 163 are some of my favourites to prepare for my family and for entertaining.)

I like to start my day with exercise for another reason, too. I find that when I have to skip my dog walk or my run for a morning—and it happens—I feel like I'm moving in slow motion all day. I'm not as alert as I could be. And that can't help but affect how I perform at my job, which, of course, is the finance part of my life (more on that aspect in Chapter 6). I am frequently a guest on television shows, these sometimes taped in front of a live audience. Whenever I'm feeling sluggish because I haven't exercised, I always also feel that my performance could have been better. But when I'm on top of my game after my workout, I feel alert and alive. And that's what viewers expect of me.

I also look fresher if I've worked out that morning. People tell me I look young for my age.

Not only am I flattered but, in my business, how one looks is important. I want to take care of my health as naturally as I can, and I believe that regular exercise has played a huge role in keeping me young both inside and out. Weight fluctuation and lack of blood flow to the skin can cause skin to lose its elasticity and plumpness over time. Looking and feeling young helps me feel confident and attractive.

Bring Along a Friend and Reconnect

Because of my hectic schedule, I don't have the time to see my friends as often as I'd like. One of the ways I've been able to keep them in my busy life is by asking each of them to join me in a physical activity and have a visit while we're at it. So occasionally one of my friends and I take a Pilates class together. Another of my friends is a runner, so once a week we jog together and have coffee afterward. And my best friend, whom I was really starting to lose touch with, plays tennis with me once a month. After the game we have a healthy lunch together. Including my friends in my fitness routine has helped me stay connected to them, and that feels great. Like so many of you, I don't have much free time, but scheduling my friends into my life has become a priority and I feel better for it.

The Mind-Body-Spirit Test

I've given you just a few examples of how fitness has influenced the six Fs in my wheel of life. To determine whether fitness is in balance with all the other aspects of my life, I apply my final test: Does my fitness solution work from each of the three personal perspectives—mind, body, and spirit? If I am intellectually sure that my fitness solution is working for me, I'm happy with it. If I physically feel, and my doctor confirms, that my fitness solution is improving my wellness, I'm happy with it. And if I feel that my fitness solution is elevating my emotional well-being, I'm happy with it.

If, having done this mind–body–spirit evaluation, I find that I am not happy, I revisit the design of my fitness solution. I have had to do this periodically. It is important to learn to listen to yourself, because only you know what really works for you on all levels. And even though it takes work to implement change, there is nothing more important and uplifting than the validation we give ourselves for getting each One Thing Right. Once you have done that, you are working with an engine that gets you where you want and deserve to be.

Fitness Solutions

A person's needs and lifestyle shape his or her fitness program, making each unique to that person. Let's look at the cases of Mary and David.

Example 1: Mary

Mary is a working mother of three young children, with little time to spare for exercise, but she has decided it is a priority for her. Both Mary's mother and aunt have had breast cancer

that has been successfully treated, and Mary is especially interested in watching her weight because of this history. After some reflection, Mary realized that—

1. She needs to lose about 25 pounds.
2. She hasn't exercised regularly in years and so needs to start out slowly to prevent injury.
3. She is on a budget and doesn't want to spend a lot of money on workout clothing or a club membership.
4. She does have a bicycle and a comfortable pair of walking shoes.
5. She thinks she would enjoy cycling and walking because she likes to exercise outdoors. The only time she has to exercise is early in the morning.
6. She believes she would be more likely to stick with an exercise program and enjoy it if she had a friend to cycle and walk with.

Mary's Fitness Solution Mary's doctor agreed with her weight-loss goal of 25 pounds and, after getting the results from her physical, told Mary moderate exercise would be great for her. This is what Mary's fitness solution looks like:

1. Mary decided to walk and cycle with a neighbourhood friend and her dog 3 mornings a week. Mary feels safer being out at 6 A.M. in her neighbourhood if she's with her dog.

> "The key to keeping motivated in any exercise routine is having a realistic plan that you can stick with."

2. She bought a membership at her local YMCA so she can lift weights once or twice a week to help improve her bone density and reduce her risk of developing osteoporosis.

3. This new exercise program, combined with a much healthier and slightly lower-calorie food program, will help Mary lose weight. She's going to keep track of her progress, and if she loses more than 2 pounds or less than 1 pound per week, she will modify her fitness and food programs accordingly to keep her weight loss at a healthy level.

Example 2: David

David is in his early forties. He is a busy man running his own small business. He works long and irregular hours and occasionally drives a truck to make business deliveries. After analyzing his physical condition, David recognized that—

1. He has no regular exercise other than playing hockey once a week in the winter and baseball twice a month in the summer.

2. He's getting more and more out of breath during his hockey games and thinks he's got about 30 pounds to lose. He just had his first high cholesterol and high blood pressure reading at his annual physical. The results were not a healthy indicator. This scared him because his dad died at age fifty-nine of a stroke, just before he was to retire.

3. He likes golf and tennis and has a membership at a club for business reasons, but his schedule isn't flexible enough to allow him to play games regularly. However, he also likes swimming and running.

David's Fitness Solution David's doctor agreed with him that along with a reduction in saturated fat intake, a fitness program with a cardiovascular element would be very beneficial; he wants to see David take off his 30 pounds of extra weight in a sensible way. The doctor has put David on medication to help deal with his high cholesterol, but the hope is that David will be able to bring his cholesterol level down soon and safely stop taking the medicine. This is what David's fitness solution looks like:

1. Along with reducing his intake of saturated fat, David has decided to cut back on his beer consumption.

2. David has found a gym with an indoor pool near his office that is open 24 hours, so he can swim, run on the treadmill, or work out with free weights whenever he has a half hour to spare.

3. David is going to keep running or walking gear in his car or the truck so that when he has downtime during the day or evening he can run or walk outdoors, wherever he is. He plans to exercise 5 days a week.

THE CASES OF Mary and David are hypothetical examples of fitness solutions developed to suit their specific needs and objectives. The following, however, is a true story of an amazing man.

My colleague's grandfather spent his adult life working as a salesman, spending long hours driving between appointments in different cities. At sixty-three he semi-retired, still suffering from the chronic back pain that had been with him for many years. Because he now had more free time, he decided that he would try riding a bicycle. His doctor had suggested he do an exercise he liked to build up his muscle mass and strength, on top of stretching and abdominal work to strengthen his back. He started out slowly, cycling short distances. Over time, he worked up to 5 kilometres, then 10 kilometres, then 20 kilometres. The loose change he happened upon while out on his bike motivated him to keep at it. Once he even found a $20 bill.

In a matter of a few months, his back pain was gone. This meant that he could indulge in his other passions—tennis and swimming. On his eightieth birthday, he took up rollerblading. Now, at the age of ninety-three, he is playing Masters tennis at the international level and golf in the Maccabiah Games—a Jewish Olympics-style competition—in Israel this year. These stories motivate me, and I hope they do the same for you.

Keeping Motivated

The key to keeping motivated in any exercise routine is making a realistic plan that you can stick to. When starting out, choose only those exercises you really enjoy. Here are a few more tips:

1. For every excuse you come up with for not exercising, try to find a solution. For example, if you say to yourself, "I'm not seeing any results," remember that it takes time to see changes. If you continue a regular workout program for at least 6 weeks, you'll see results. If your excuse is that you always feel sore from exercise, take a break and change exercises: either you're working too hard or too often. Some soreness from working out muscles you haven't used in a while occurs at the beginning, but it shouldn't be long before you're feeling only a good fatigue, with no pain.

2. At first, plan short, realistic goals so that you are sure to succeed. No half marathons to start!

3. Exercise at a place where you know you'll go (this might even be your home).

4. Do a variety of exercises. Variety will prevent boredom and injury.

5. If you have to miss a few days of exercise, don't feel guilty and abandon your program altogether. Just get back to a regular routine as soon as possible.

6. Make your exercise sessions short and effective.

Recording and Reviewing Your Progress

To make sure you're on track with your fitness solution, record your progress in a fitness journal. I've included a sample at the end of this chapter. On the same calendar that you blocked off your exercise schedule, mark down each time you actually exercised, what you did, and for how long. Also note how you felt when you started and when you finished. At the end of each month, when you review your progress, check whether you are achieving your goals at the pace you had projected. If you didn't stick to your program regularly, evaluate why not. Maybe the times were not convenient. If you were exhausted each time you began exercising, you probably didn't have as effective a workout as you could have, so you may need to change the time of your workout. All this information will allow you to fine-tune your schedule to make it work better for you the next month. At first, perfecting your program may be by trial and error, but keep at it and you will soon find a routine that works for you.

Re-evaluating Your Fitness Solution

Whatever your situation is, you are the one in charge of your fitness solution. *You* will decide what type of exercise will work for you to get to where you want to be. And you will decide at what point you have achieved those goals. It's a good idea to re-evaluate your program every three months, making the changes necessary to keep it well balanced and challenging. Once you have achieved your fitness objectives, again re-evaluate the program. You may decide to continue with your current program because it is working well for you, or you may need to make adjustments to accommodate your changes in taste and fitness level. In this way your fitness solution can evolve to incorporate new aspects of your life and reach new objectives.

my fitness journal

week 1

Exercise _____

Duration _____

Time of Day _____

How Do I Feel? (e.g., energy level, my diet, my hydration)

_____

_____

_____

_____

_____

Total days exercised _____

End of Week comments:

_____

_____

_____

_____

_____

_____

_____

_____

_____

_____

week 2

Exercise _____

Duration _____

Time of Day _____

How Do I Feel? (e.g., energy level, my diet, my hydration)

_____

_____

_____

_____

_____

Total days exercised _____

End of Week comments:

_____

_____

_____

_____

_____

_____

_____

_____

week 3

Exercise _____

Duration _____

Time of Day _____

How Do I Feel? (e.g., energy level, my diet, my hydration)

_____

_____

_____

_____

_____

Total days exercised _____

End of Week comments:

_____

_____

_____

_____

_____

_____

_____

_____

week 4

Exercise _____

Duration _____

Time of Day _____

How Do I Feel? (e.g., energy level, my diet,
my hydration)

_____

_____

_____

_____

_____

Total days exercised _____

End of Week comments:

_____

_____

_____

_____

_____

_____

_____

_____

week 5

Exercise _____

Duration _____

Time of Day _____

How Do I Feel? (e.g., energy level, my diet,
my hydration)

_____

_____

_____

_____

_____

Total days exercised _____

End of Week comments:

_____

_____

_____

_____

_____

_____

_____

_____

week 6

Exercise _____

Duration _____

Time of Day _____

How Do I Feel? (e.g., energy level, my diet,
my hydration)

_____

_____

_____

_____

_____

Total days exercised _____

End of Week comments:

_____

_____

_____

_____

_____

_____

_____

_____

_____

_____

week 7

Exercise _____

Duration _____

Time of Day _____

How Do I Feel? (e.g., energy level, my diet,
my hydration)

_____

_____

_____

_____

_____

Total days exercised _____

End of Week comments:

_____

_____

_____

_____

_____

_____

_____

_____

_____

_____

food
eating the healthy way

food eating the healthy way

During years of experimenting with what and how much I ate, I realized that when I included a variety of foods that were balanced and moderate in portion size, I felt my best. I had the energy that it took to carry on all my tasks in my day. Food is the one segment of life we all share on a daily basis. Food brings family and friends together. And when you combine a healthy diet with an active lifestyle, you feel and look better, which makes the other segments of your life easier to manage. It's all about balancing the wheel of life.

But, as it is for many of us, food is an emotionally charged issue for me. Food can make us feel better—it's comforting and pleasurable—and it makes us feel satisfied inside when life does not. That is the trap food represents. If we feel empty for an emotional reason, food can fill us up—at least for the short term. But, unlike other guilty pleasures—alcohol or cigarettes for instance— we can't live without food. We can't quit cold turkey like we can with certain vices … because food is not a vice; it is vital for living. So in order

to live a healthy life, we must learn to manage and moderate our eating. Like most of us, I learned early on that constant dieting is not a healthy or sustainable option. I began a twenty-year quest to find a workable, long-term, healthy but still varied and delicious eating solution, and, having found it, I am passionate about sharing it with others.

Part of my commitment to spreading my eating philosophy comes from the knowledge that our children learn from what they see us

"Statistics show that the children of parents with healthy lifestyles are substantially more likely to become healthy adults themselves."

doing, more so even than from what they hear us saying. If we all get off the couch and start moving, if we start eating more fruits and vegetables, our kids will notice. Statistics show that the children of parents with healthy lifestyles are substantially more likely to become healthy adults themselves.

The other factor that has made me committed to my eating solution and philosophy is my weight: Controlling it is something I've had to work at all my life. I was overweight as a child, growing up on a high-fat diet that had an abundance of simple carbohydrates but was low in fruits and vegetables. When I got my health wake-up call in my early thirties, in the form of a high blood cholesterol reading at my yearly checkup, I knew I had to take action. Exercising every day wasn't enough. In my case, my diet was the culprit and that was where I needed to make significant changes. I owed it to myself, and to my family, to make my own wellness a priority.

It's all about balancing input with output; in other words, calories in and calories out. For most of us, that's a simple equation. Food is fuel, and you need to burn more fuel through exercise and everyday living than you take in, in order to

lose weight. The rate at which you burn that fuel is the rate of your metabolism. But we all know that the real challenge is the practical reality of managing your weight. That is highly personalized and, as we all know, not always easy.

As I mentioned in the Introduction to this book, what I became aware of after my high cholesterol scare was that my body can register a healthy weight and yet not be healthy. I had been conditioned to believe that being thin and looking good was the goal, when what I should have been thinking about was being strong and well. I realized that it's just as important to focus on the quality of the food you eat as it is the quantity. I had to start eating a balanced and varied diet to provide my body with quality fuel. The body uses more than calories to fuel it efficiently. Supplying your body with a poor diet is like running a car on low-octane fuel and no oil. A healthy diet does for the body what clean oil and premium high-octane fuel does for a car.

Many of us put ourselves through an enormous amount of angst and stress trying to be thin. There is so much pressure in our society, especially on women, about appearance. It's everywhere—in magazines, in movies, on television. "Weightism" is one of the few prejudices that our society still tolerates. While most of us would agree that it's unfair the way people who have a serious weight problem are scorned, there doesn't seem to be any relief for them in sight. The North American diet industry is a multibillion-dollar-a-year business, and it is profiting heavily from both the obesity epidemic and society's preoccupation with thinness. There are hundreds of fad diets that promote the idea that you will be acceptable to society only if you shed weight—down to an unrealistic ideal, and at an unhealthy rate of loss. Of course, not all diets are unhealthy, but most fad diets have little or nothing to do with health and, even with those that do have some merit, the weight eventually comes back. In fact, the worst of the fad diets can be downright dangerous. As you can tell, I don't think much of them; at my core, I'm a believer in finding a healthy and sensible long-term eating regimen rather than a quick fix.

Once you stop a quick-fix diet, you'll gain back the weight you lost, and probably more. Put a few of these diets back to back and … if your body weight feels like a yo-yo, your self-esteem will be even worse.

A Long-Term Healthy Solution

What's really important to talk about is how to get ourselves on the right track to a sustainable, healthy, life-long eating solution. Whether you have lots of weight to lose, a few pounds to shed, or you are already at a comfortable weight but would like to be healthier, my approach will help you find an eating solution that improves both your wellness and nutrition. If you are already eating a well-balanced and healthy diet, the advice and tips I give will reinforce your daily regime. There's no magic or gimmick to my method—I believe in simple, easy, quick to prepare, widely varied, and delicious food. I've included many balanced recipes for you in this book, starting on page 163. And by understanding the philosophy that underlies those recipes, which I explain below, you'll also be able to eat out healthfully at any establishment. My solution simply involves making a commitment to healthier choices, choosing foods from the four food groups, eating the right quantities of healthy foods at the right times, and sticking with this approach long enough to see the results. By choosing the right foods, you'll get the vitamins, minerals, and energy you need from your food to feel great. Successful eating consists of balance and moderation. Add in an active lifestyle and you'll find it easier to maintain a healthy body weight.

Now, let's get started by considering a few questions.

Supplying your body with a poor diet is like running a car on low-octane fuel and no oil. A healthy diet does for the body what clean oil and premium high-octane fuel does for a car.

where am I now?

Do I feel strong, energized, alert, and ready to go every morning when I wake up?

☐ Yes ☐ No

Do I eat foods from at least three, and preferably four, of the major food groups at every meal? (I'll tell you why you should do so below.)

☐ Yes ☐ No

Do I eat a nutritious breakfast?

☐ Yes ☐ No

Do I eat regularly throughout the day?

☐ Yes ☐ No

Do I include healthy snacks between meals?

☐ Yes ☐ No

Do I eat healthfully when I'm on holidays and away from home?

☐ Yes ☐ No

Am I at a comfortable and healthy weight for me?

☐ Yes ☐ No

Do I feel healthy?

☐ Yes ☐ No

Current weight: _____

If you answered yes to most of the questions above, chances are that you are eating well and enjoying the success of your good habits. If not, then you have some work to do toward better health. Now, some questions about your family health history:

What conditions and diseases are found in my family history?

Alzheimer's disease   ☐ Yes   ☐ No

Cancer   ☐ Yes   ☐ No

Diabetes/hypoglycemia
(insulin/sugar-based sensitivity)   ☐ Yes   ☐ No

Heart disease   ☐ Yes   ☐ No

High blood pressure   ☐ Yes   ☐ No

Obesity   ☐ Yes   ☐ No

Osteoporosis or osteoarthritis   ☐ Yes   ☐ No

Stroke   ☐ Yes   ☐ No

If you answered yes to any of these conditions, you should look closely at the way you are eating and possibly rethink your food choices.

As when you analyzed your fitness needs in Chapter 1, the last question to ask yourself is: Even if I *feel* well, do I know for sure that I *am* well? Again, having your doctor do a complete physical examination on you is the only way to accurately answer this question and to determine your overall health. Your doctor will also help you define a healthy weight for yourself. Do not skip this step. (You may already have booked your physical or even completed it if you are embarking on a new fitness program.)

Physical examination completed on (date):

_____

Results of physical:

Cholesterol reading
Below normal ☐   Normal ☐   Above normal ☐

Blood pressure
Below normal ☐   Normal ☐   Above normal ☐

Weight
Below normal ☐   Normal ☐   Above normal ☐

Stress test (electrocardiogram)
Below normal ☐   Normal ☐   Above normal ☐

Stress test (with exercise)
Below normal ☐   Normal ☐   Above normal ☐

Doctor's recommendations:

_____

_____

_____

Inform your doctor that you are thinking about trying to follow the four food groups eating plan, with a focus on lower fat, lower sugar, more complex carbohydrates, and high-fibre foods. This is an "everything in moderation, nothing forbidden" eating plan. Your doctor will likely endorse this balanced diet regime and may suggest you look for support by way of a nutritionist or group environment that supports this approach to weight loss.

The Food Journal

One of the tools to get you started on the right path is a food journal. Keeping track of your food intake can be time-consuming, but it's an important tool in understanding your eating patterns. Even if you are focused on healthy eating rather than eating to lose weight, a food journal can be informative, helping you see where you can make better nutrition choices. Keep the journal for at least one month so you fully understand your weight-loss or -gain patterns. Weigh yourself once a week and record this weight in your fitness journal. It's always best to weigh yourself at the same time each week, ideally in the morning before you have eaten. For the most accurate results, wear the same weight in clothing.

Research shows that those who successfully keep their weight off are those who initially kept track of their food intake on a daily basis. On page 46 there is a sample food journal for one day. At the end of this chapter, on page 66, you will find a weekly food journal to get you started on healthy eating. The journal allows you to make better choices by looking at the big picture. (Understanding food groups and serving sizes, which I discuss in the section below, is an important tool when it comes to analyzing your food journal.) Once you feel you have your eating routine under control, you can stop recording in the journal. But if the weight creeps back on, start recording again.

The other thing that's important to keep track of in your journal is your water intake. I find that often when I feel like I just have to have a snack, it turns out I'm thirsty, not hungry. Although authorities have differing theories about how much water humans require, most agree that we normally need to consume 6 to 8 cups of water daily. If you're exercising and perspiring, it may be substantially more than that. You need to take that amount of water into your system every day in your diet—whether it be through drinking water, juice, or even decaffeinated coffee or tea, or eating fruits and vegetables—or you can become chronically constipated—a significant sign that your body is not effectively regulating itself. That can certainly hurt weight loss and can also affect long-term colon, liver, kidney, and skin health. Our body is 70 percent water, and our bodies need to maintain that amount at all times. This means that if you're not drinking enough water, your body will retain water—translating into more pounds on the scale.

Review the results of your physical examination, your answers to the questions on pages 40 and 41, and your journal notes, and you will understand where you are now.

Research shows that those who successfully keep their weight off are those who initially kept track of their food intake on a daily basis.

my food journal

MORNING 6 A.M.–11 A.M.

FOOD	AMOUNT
Protein (meat and alternatives)	2 eggs, 1 oz cheese
Breads/grains	2 slices bread
Fruits/vegetables	apple, carrots and low-fat dip
Dairy	3/4 cup low-fat yogourt
Water	1 cup
Other beverages	2 coffees, 1 green tea
Fats/sugars	1 tbsp peanut butter, 2 tsp sugar in coffee

Comments: Good morning, was not hungry and had energy

MIDDAY 11 A.M.–3 P.M.

FOOD	AMOUNT
Protein (meat and alternatives)	3 oz chicken
Breads/grains	1 pita pocket
Fruits/vegetables	sliced cucumber, tomatoes, lettuce
Dairy	4 oz frozen yogourt
Water	2 cups
Other beverages	1 can diet cola
Fats/sugars	2 tbsp low-fat mayonnaise, 1 low-fat oatmeal cookie

Comments: Felt satisfied

LATE AFTERNOON 3 P.M.–6 P.M.

FOOD	AMOUNT
Protein (meat and alternatives)	1/4 cup almonds
Breads/grains	4 Melba toasts
Fruits/vegetables	1 orange, crudités with low-fat dip
Dairy	1 oz low-fat cheese string
Water	0
Other beverages	1 green tea
Fats/sugars	2 pieces black licorice

Comments: Grazed all afternoon, felt satisfied

TOTAL PROTEINS:	5
TOTAL BREADS/GRAINS:	7
TOTAL FRUITS/VEGETABLES:	7
TOTAL DAIRY:	3
TOTAL WATER:	4
TOTAL BEVERAGES (OTHER THAN WATER):	6
TOTAL FATS AND SUGARS:	5

DAY'S EXERCISE, INCLUDING DURATION:
30 minutes stationary bike, 5 minutes stretching

STRESS LEVEL (RATE ON A SCALE OF 0 TO 5): 3

DAY'S COMMENTS: Should have drunk more water. Try to cut down on soft drinks and increase herbal teas. Generally great day, happy with exercise.

WEEKLY WEIGHT: _____

EVENING 6 P.M.–10 P.M.

FOOD	AMOUNT
Protein (meat and alternatives)	4 oz grilled salmon
Breads/grains	1 cup brown rice
Fruits/vegetables	1 cup strawberries, grilled bell peppers
Dairy	0
Water	1 cup
Other beverages	1 can diet cola
Fats/sugars	1 oz chocolate

Comments: Was hungry at 10 P.M.; didn't drink enough water

where do I want to be?

Put aside all your insecurities and fears about what anybody else thinks; don't let a partner or fashion magazine influence you. This is just for you. Picture your healthiest, strongest, most confident self. What does that look and feel like? It's in this frame of mind that you want to envision your realistic, healthy, and comfortable weight. If your weight doesn't need to change, think about feeling as strong and well as you possibly can.

Ask yourself these questions:

Am I ready to start eating better?

☐ Yes   ☐ No

Do I have a well-thought-out plan?

☐ Yes   ☐ No

What is my reason for losing weight?

_____

_____

_____

Do I think eating well will make me a happier person?   ☐ Yes   ☐ No

If yes, why? _____

_____

_____

_____

If I failed before at eating better, what will I now do differently?

_____

_____

_____

Do I eat because I'm hungry or to comfort myself?   ☐ Hunger   ☐ Comfort

Do I seem to always think about what I'm going to eat and what I've eaten?   ☐ Yes   ☐ No

What is my overall focus?

Lose weight   ☐ Yes   ☐ No

Firm up, reduce body fat   ☐ Yes   ☐ No

Improve overall health   ☐ Yes   ☐ No

All of the above   ☐ Yes   ☐ No

What is my ideal, healthy goal for each of these?

Healthy weight _____

Body fat % _____
(BMI—ask a professional)

Other (health improvement) _____

What is the difference between my goal and my current weight? _____

Your answers to these questions will determine how serious you are this time around about maintaining your weight loss and whether you are motivated for the right reasons or whether you need to do more self-examination.

Food Groups

The first step in eating well involves getting educated about food by understanding the basic food groups: grains, fruits and vegetables, dairy products, and meat and alternatives. Up-to-date food guides include information on how good nutrition can prevent disease. They also factor in legumes, whole grains, seeds and nuts, fish, and even plant oils such as olive oil as part of a healthy diet. Current food guides will also differentiate between which of the kinds of foods within the food groups are better for you—for example, leaner meats and fish, whole and low-glycemic grains such as barley, quinoa, and brown rice (low-glycemic foods are those that take longer to digest, raising blood sugar slowly and keeping you feeling full longer), and which fruits and vegetables have the greatest nutrient benefits. Low-fat dairy products are also emphasized.

The Canada Food Guide for Healthy Eating is being revised. The existing Canada Food Guide recommends that adults consume the following numbers of servings for each food group daily:

Food Group	One Serving
Grains: 5–12 servings	1 slice toast; 3/4 cup cereal; 1/2 small bagel, pita, or bun; 1 cup pasta or rice
Fruits and vegetables: 5–10 servings	1 medium-sized fruit or vegetable; 1/2 cup canned or frozen vegetables or fruit; 1 cup green salad; 1/2 cup juice
Meat and alternatives: 3–4 servings	3 oz chicken, beef, or fish; 1/2 cup beans; 2 tablespoons peanut butter; 1–2 eggs
Dairy products: 2–3 servings	2 slices packaged cheese; 3/4 cup yogourt; 1 cup low-fat milk

The United States Department of Agriculture has recently released its Food Guide Pyramid (see www.MyPyramid.gov). It is a great tool to help you personalize your eating plan, taking your age, sex, and daily amount of exercise into account. It stresses that each person needs 30 minutes of moderate or vigorous exercise every day for good health. The pyramid is divided into six bands, each a different width and representing the proportion of food you should eat from that food group. The largest band represents grains. Vegetables, dairy products, and fruits come next in terms of the proportion of one's diet they should represent, and then meats and beans, with oils representing the smallest food group required daily in a healthy diet. Again, how much of each food group you should eat daily depends on your age and exercise level, among other factors.

A good rule of thumb when planning your meals is to include something from at least three and preferably four of the major food groups in each main meal and at least two food groups in each snack. Many people don't believe that they can manage this easily or without eating too many calories at a time. But it's not as tough as it sounds. For example, here is what a healthy breakfast might consist of:

- Bowl of high-fibre cereal with low-fat milk

- Small apple or banana

- Small handful (about 1/4 cup) of unsalted almonds

or

- 1/2 cup of low-fat yogourt

- Small bowl of berries

- Boiled or poached egg with 1 slice unbuttered whole-grain toast

If you break down each of these breakfasts into its food groups, you will see that all of the major food groups are represented. A healthy mid-morning snack might be:

- 1 oz low-fat cheese

- 4 high-fibre crackers

- Small fruit or cut vegetables with a low-fat dip

This snack encompasses three food groups.

Combining two or three of the food groups in each meal keeps you satisfied much longer than if you eat only carbs or fruit for breakfast. These major food groups are grain products—preferably whole grains, fruits and vegetables, dairy products, and meat and alternatives, including fish, poultry, eggs, and meat substitutes such as beans, legumes, and soy.

Emphasizing fruits and vegetables and complex grains in your diet is the most nutritious way to eat. And I believe it is the most successful route for permanent and safe weight loss. These foods are loaded with nutritional value. They contain fibre, which is important for colon health and also keeps you feeling satiated. All three are low in calories and fat. If you use fruits and vegetables and complex grains as the foundation of your diet, adding lean protein, dairy, and fat last, you will be amazed at how well you will feel and how reaching your healthy body weight will be more easily attainable. And from a food preparation perspective, your options are endless. The perfectly balanced plate consists of 50 percent non-starchy vegetables, 25 percent protein, and 25 percent grain or starchy vegetable. If you're dining out at an Italian restaurant or a steak house, for example, this balance may not be practical, but it is something you should aim for on a regular basis.

One last note: It is unwise to omit any of the four food groups entirely. Unless you have a food allergy, which is a serious condition, you need the nutrients from each food group to maintain good health.

Now that we understand the major food groups, let's take a look at the specific components that make up our food: calories, and our daily diet's building blocks: carbohydrate, protein, and fat.

Calories

A calorie is the amount of energy that food provides. To achieve an ideal weight you must take in only the number of calories your body needs—no more, no less. The number of calories you need daily depends on your age, activity level, and body frame. Calorie intake for women trying to lose weight will be in the 1600 to 2200 calorie range; for men, in the 2000 to 2800 calorie range. Of course, this varies from person to person, and you will have to find what works for you. Some people just have a quicker metabolism than others. But, in general, the more you exercise, the more calories you burn. And the more lean muscle mass you have, the more efficiently you burn calories. We lose lean muscle mass as we age or become less active.

Now that you have some idea of how many calories you need daily to maintain a healthy body weight, how do you apply this knowledge to the various food groups? Opposite is a list of the four major food groups and the various numbers of servings for three calorie intakes. This is an approximate calculation; the numbers will vary depending on the type and quality of food eaten. You may want to have on hand as a reference a good calorie-counting book detailing the calories of various foods.

Servings According to Daily Calorie Intake			
	1500 CALORIES	2000 CALORIES	2600 CALORIES
Grains	6 servings	9 servings	12 servings
Fruits and vegetables	6 servings	8 servings	10 servings
Dairy products	3 servings	3 servings	4 servings
Meat and alternatives	2 servings	2–3 servings	3 servings

Carbohydrates

When eating carbohydrates, your body's main energy source, the key is to choose complex carbohydrates rather than simple carbohydrates, the ones found in non-nutritional sugar and white-flour products such as cakes, doughnuts, and cookies—what I call empty calorie foods. Complex carbohydrates, found in fruits, vegetables, grains, legumes, and dairy products, keep your blood sugar stable by releasing glucose into the blood slowly, helping you feel full longer. They make up a healthy low-fat diet and can reduce the risk of heart disease, stroke, diabetes, and some types of cancers.

When choosing grains, it's best to stick to whole grains. They contain fibre, vitamins, and phytochemicals. They also help control blood sugar and may help prevent type 2 diabetes. Whole grains in the form of brown rice, barley, or rye still contain the natural bran and germ. Refined grains, such as white rice and the grains found in most breads and pasta, have the bran and germ removed during processing. The only way to know for sure if the product you buy is whole grain is to read the label. The first ingredient should be whole-wheat flour, oats, brown rice, or whole-rye flour.

Carbohydrates are one of the most controversial foods around. At one time, grains were thought to be the food that would keep us lean. But by the start of the 1990s, people were not losing but gaining weight on carbs. It was at this time that several diet movements surfaced, blaming carbs for the rise of obesity in our society. The truth is that portion size and quality were the cause of carbohydrates' bad reputation. The healthier complex carbohydrates such as brown rice, ancient grains, and fruits and vegetables were not the culprits. Certain fad diets had told us that we could eat as many carbohydrates as we liked as long as we cut the fat from our diet. But carbohydrates do contain calories, and more calories than your body needs, whether from carbs, fat, or protein, will always result in excess weight.

Glycemic Index

Complex carbohydrates differ in nutritional value. Some are converted to blood sugar quickly while others take longer. Complex carbs are classified in terms of glycemic index (GI), which indicates their ability to cause a rise in blood sugar. *Foods that have a low GI raise blood sugar slowly*, keeping you feeling full longer and therefore helping you control your weight. *Those with a high GI raise your blood sugar quickly*, leaving you hungry sooner; these foods can contribute to weight gain if you eat too much of them.

Foods that have a high glycemic index include:

- bananas, watermelon, mango, pineapple, raisins
- carrots, corn
- Corn Flakes, Cheerios
- pasta, couscous, white rice
- pretzels, popcorn, potato chips
- rice cakes, white-flour crackers, bagels, white bread and rolls, cakes
- sugar, chocolate, honey

Foods that have a low glycemic index include:

- apples, pears, cherries, grapefruit, plums, peaches
- sweet potatoes, beans, peas
- lentils, soybeans, peanuts, brown rice, bulgur, barley
- milk, yogourt, soy milk
- oatmeal, All-Bran, Red River cereals

All complex carbohydrates have excellent nutritional value, whether they have a high or low glycemic index. Don't avoid those with a high glycemic index—just don't count on them to fill you up if you're looking for a sustained energy boost.

Fibre

The jewel found in carbohydrates is fibre. Fibre has been shown to lower cholesterol, lessen the risk of heart disease, prevent bowel problems, reduce the risk of colon cancer, help control type 2 diabetes, and help in weight loss.

There are two types of fibre: *soluble* and *insoluble*. Soluble fibre is found in oats, barley, vegetables, fruit, brown rice, and oat bran, among other foods. This type of fibre decreases blood cholesterol, thereby possibly decreasing the risk of heart disease. Insoluble fibre is found in foods such as wheat and corn bran, and in fruits and vegetables as well. This type of fibre helps promote regularity, which can decrease the risk of colon cancer. Eating foods with fibre will make you feel full longer and more satisfied. Foods that contain soluble fibre have a low glycemic index, which means your blood sugar rises relatively slowly, keeping you feeling full longer.

Studies indicate that the more fibre you consume, the lower your risk of heart attack. Most North Americans consume about 11 grams of fibre daily. The National Cancer Institute recommends eating between 25 and 35 grams daily. Two effective ways to increase your fibre are to increase your vegetable intake, and to reduce the amount of refined white-flour products in your daily diet while increasing your intake of whole grains. Increase your fibre intake slowly or you'll have side effects of feeling bloated, gassy, or crampy, or diarrhea.

Foods considered high in fibre are those that contain at least 4 grams of fibre per serving. Foods containing 6 grams or more are very high in fibre. An apple, pear, and orange each contain about 4 grams of fibre; a banana, about 3 grams. A medium-sized sweet potato contains about 7 grams, while a baked potato with skin has 5 grams, and 1/2 cup of green beans, 4 grams. And here's an eye-opener: A slice of 100 percent whole-wheat bread boasts 6 grams of fibre, while a slice of white bread has only 1 gram. Legumes are also excellent sources of fibre: 1/2 cup of cooked kidney beans or chickpeas contains 6 grams.

Sugar and Sweeteners

When I have food cravings, it's almost always for sugary foods—cookies, ice cream, cake, or chocolate. Sugar is closely tied to my emotional state. When I'm happy, sad, excited, or overwhelmed, I crave sweets.

Statistics show that the average North American consumes about 120 pounds of sugar per year. That's about 40 teaspoons of sugar daily. Yet the recommended daily amount is only 6 teaspoons. Sugar comes in many forms: sucrose, glucose, lactose, maltose, molasses, honey, corn syrup, brown sugar, to name a few. They are all equally nutritious, except for molasses, which contains B vitamins, calcium, and potassium—nutrients the other sugars don't have. Fructose, a form of sugar which is not as refined as the other types, has twice the sweetness of regular sugar, so you can decrease the amount you use by about half. Honey and brown sugar are not more nutritious than white sugar.

Some researchers are attempting to make the correlation between excessive sugar in our diet and obesity, heart disease, high blood pressure, a rise in triglyceride levels, depression, mood swings, blood sugar problems, gallstones, kidney problems, and diabetes. However, there is no direct proof that sugar causes these diseases but only that it may precipitate them.

There is no reason to severely restrict your sugar intake unless you have diabetes and are carbohydrate sensitive, a condition in which consuming too many high glycemic carbs triggers hunger and overeating. The problem with sugar is that it is an empty carbohydrate, with excess calories. It stimulates the release of insulin, the hormone that moves energy in the form of sugar to our cells. But excess insulin in the body causes the body to transform excess calories to fat. Insulin also can trigger a sugar high or a sugar low reaction. If you are having a sugar low, or hypoglycemia, you crave more sugary foods, which can leave you feeling unwell and lead to mood swings. To prevent this, combine your sugar with foods high in fibre and/or protein to delay the sugar's entry into the bloodstream. Drinking water whenever you eat sugary foods may also help dilute or reduce their effect on your energy level.

Over a lifetime of consuming excessively sugary foods, many people develop a condition called insulin resistance. This means that the insulin your body produces isn't getting sugar from your bloodstream into your cells, where it should be burned off or stored as necessary fuel. This can lead to diabetes, among other illnesses.

Not surprisingly, foods such as candy, chewing gum, cakes, cereals, cookies, jams, chocolate, non-diet soft drinks, and artificially flavoured juice-type drinks contain large amounts of sugar. Be aware, too, that many foods contain hidden sugar: Beets, carrots, corn, refined white-flour products, white rice, ketchup, barbecue sauce, and salad dressing are all sugary, high glycemic foods.

There are many substitutes for refined sugar. What used to be known as an artificial sweetener is now called a sugar substitute or a low-calorie sweetener simply because the word *artificial* has a negative connotation. These sweeteners can be found in chewing gum, yogourt, beverages, cakes, chocolate bars, candies, and more. They have been around for decades but, despite this, haven't put an end to obesity—possibly because those who consume artificial sweeteners or artificially sweetened foods consume these missing calories elsewhere, usually in higher fat foods.

Artificial sweeteners when used in moderation are fine. Just don't depend on them to eliminate excess calories from beverages, desserts, or your meals in your overall diet. Most foods containing artificial sweeteners are usually of poor nutritional value. Their only advantage is that they don't cause tooth decay and they offer a sugar alternative to people with diabetes. I recommend using Splenda, a natural sugar substitute derived from sugar. But whereas a cup of sugar has 200 grams of carbohydrates, Splenda has only 25 grams per cup. It's perfect for those on a calorie- or carbohydrate-reduced diet and for those with diabetes.

The bottom line is that regular intake of sugar does not promote obesity, heart disease, or diabetes. It's the overuse of sugar that leads to these problems.

Proteins

Your body needs protein to build and maintain muscle tissue and for cell repairs. It maintains strong bones, produces enzymes to help digest your food, and allows your brain to see, hear, and think. Protein also boosts your metabolism and fills your stomach so you won't feel hungry. The key to fitting protein into your diet is to include a variety of sources of lean protein such as lean beef and pork, chicken or turkey breast, fish, and tofu.

Allow yourself 4 to 6 ounces of protein at your lunch and dinner meals. Snacks should include protein in the form of yogourt, a small amount of nuts, or milk or soy beverage. But be aware that if you consume too much protein that is not lean, you're increasing your amounts of saturated fat, cholesterol, and calories. Meat, even lean meat, contains saturated fat and cholesterol, which can cause heart disease and stroke. The excess fat in meat can also lead to obesity and certain kinds of cancer, among other diseases. So eat the higher fat and saturated protein in moderation, alternating it with other forms of protein such as fish, beans, and soy products, which contain no saturated fat.

If you fill up on non-lean protein, you also won't be leaving yourself room for the lower fat choices such as fruits, vegetables, and grains, which also provide essential nutrition. Instead of serving a meat entree that could contain as much as 12 ounces of protein, try just adding small amounts of meat to your salads, pastas, and soups. This is the ideal way to get just enough protein in your diet. (Again, when I warn against consuming excess protein, I'm usually referring to animal protein such as meat, chicken, and cheese. I treat myself to larger portions of fish and soy products.)

Meat, fish, poultry, eggs, soy products, and dairy products are all complete proteins, which means that these foods contains all twenty essential amino acids. An incomplete protein does not contain all twenty. Foods that are incomplete proteins include grains, legumes, beans, nuts, and seeds. The good news is that you can make incomplete proteins complete by combining them. For example, a piece of bread with peanut butter makes a complete protein. Any grain combined with beans makes a complete protein. And you don't have to combine a grain and bean in one meal to make a complete protein: You can eat each separately if you like, as long as they're both eaten in the same day.

Fat

We are a fat-phobic society, yet certain fats are necessary for good health. These fats play an important role in hormone production, red blood cell formation, joint lubrication, and proper insulin function. Eating the right fats in moderation will not cause you to gain excess fat. Too many people are obsessed with taking all the fat out of their diet, which is unhealthy. A healthy diet should consist of a daily intake of between 25 and 30 percent fat. However, the typical North American diet, which consists of 40 percent or more fat, exceeds that considerably.

Fat has more calories per gram than protein or carbohydrates: 9 calories per gram versus only 4 calories per gram. And fat doesn't fill you up the same way that protein and carbs do, which means you're hungry soon after you've eaten fatty foods. It's also important to be aware that low fat does not mean no fat. Low- or no-fat products can still be loaded with calories. And a calorie is a calorie. Aim to keep your fat intake to less than 30 percent of your total daily calories and your saturated fat intake to less than 10 percent.

Saturated fat is found in animal products—meat, chicken, and dairy products. These fats in excess can clog your arteries and lead to heart disease and stroke. Trans fat is also a fat to watch out for. This type of fat is produced when unsaturated fat is hydrogenated, a manufacturing process that changes a liquid fat into a solid. Foods are often hydrogenated to preserve them or to change their texture. Many types of margarine contain hydrogenated fat. If you're eating a diet based on fast food or packaged and preserved foods, you are probably getting too much trans fat in your diet. Try to avoid foods that list hydrogenated vegetable oil or coconut or palm oil on the ingredient label. Cookies, granola bars, dips, chips, frozen dinners, ready-to-bake rolls, and frozen desserts are often high in trans fat. Read the labels on your food products. Many food manufacturers are now eliminating the trans fats from their products, substituting monounsaturated or polyunsaturated vegetable oil.

No discussion of saturated fat would be complete without mentioning its major impact on cholesterol levels. The liver makes all the cholesterol you need for proper health. Excess cholesterol from food is transported to the blood and, over years, clogs the arteries. The amount of cholesterol appropriate for good health is 300 milligrams daily. Most people get much more—the yolk of a single egg has almost that much cholesterol. The foods that contain cholesterol are animal based—meat and poultry, eggs, and dairy products. Plant foods contain no cholesterol.

So stick to the healthier monounsaturated and polyunsaturated fats. Monounsaturated fats are the healthiest. Canola, olive, and peanut oil are monounsaturated fats. These fats reduce blood cholesterol by increasing the good type of blood cholesterol (HDL). Polyunsaturated fats contain essential fatty acids, which help maintain proper brain functioning and hormone production and can lower cholesterol and triglyceride (blood fat) levels, reduce blood pressure, and improve the health of your skin and hair. You can find essential fatty acids in foods rich in omega-3 and omega-6 fats. Omega-6 is found in oils,

> "Your body thrives when it has a steady amount of nutritious food and will burn calories more efficiently."

nuts, and margarine and is easy to get enough of. Omega-3 is not as common. Flaxseed oil is one of the best sources of omega-3. It is also found in fatty fish (such as salmon, tuna, and mackerel), walnut oil, and some leafy green vegetables, such as spinach, bok choy, and kale.

Hidden Fats

Even though you may be watching your butter, egg, and meat intake, keep in mind that many foods contain hidden saturated fat. We all know about visible fats: butter, margarine, oils, sour cream, ice cream, cheese, peanut butter, sauces, and the fat on meat. But there is hidden fat in foods you may have never thought of. Deli meats, store-baked goods, chocolate bars, pizza with the works, quiche, marinated salads, fast foods, and fried foods all have loads of fat. If you're wondering why you're unable to lose weight or lower your cholesterol even though you are cutting out the visible fats from your diet, take a closer look at those hidden fat foods; they may be the problem. Again, the motto is balance and moderation.

Losing Your Fat Taste Buds

We usually overindulge in high-fat foods because of their mouth feel. They taste good, smell wonderful, and feel good in our mouths. To successfully reduce your fat intake, you must be willing to make permanent dietary changes and re-educate your taste buds. This doesn't mean deprivation. As you begin to eat lower fat foods you will gradually lose your fat taste buds. I find that if I eat too many high-fat foods my body reacts negatively. Not only do I feel bloated and sluggish, but I have an unpleasant aftertaste the next morning. Give yourself at least 6 weeks of eating lower fat healthier foods to notice the difference.

Portion Size

For me, the way to maintain consistent energy and keep from overeating is to graze throughout the day. That seems to be a healthy way to eat for many people. I feel deprived if I wait more than 3 hours to eat, and it's hard to keep my portions in control if I'm very hungry. But grazing doesn't mean that I am constantly eating—something that would be very easy to do since I am often around food in my work. Grazing is eating often during the day to keep feeling satisfied and never overly hungry. Graze on fruit, vegetables, and other nutritionally high but lower calorie and lower fat foods. If you don't want to eat that often, I would urge you to at least make sure you eat three meals per day. If you can, throw in a piece of fruit and cheese for an occasional snack between meals. Your body thrives when it has a steady supply of nutritious fuel and will ultimately burn calories more efficiently.

For those who want to lose weight, portion sizing is essential. It certainly seems to be a weak spot for many of us in North America. Restaurant portions have not helped us to understand appropriate food quantities. The movie *Super Size Me* got everyone talking about how fast-food restaurants are making our society fat with their giant "value" meals. But since most of us eat the majority of our meals at home, not in fast-food restaurants, we can't blame McDonald's or Burger King for quantities we eat at our own dinner table. It is important to familiarize yourself with the appropriate portion size for each type of food. The various food guides are a good place to start educating yourself. You'll be amazed how a proper portion-sized meal satisfies you when you're eating nutritiously and regularly throughout the day. It's only when you skip meals or eat non-nutritious foods that these portions seem so small. Remember, the well-balanced meal consists of one-quarter protein, one-quarter carbohydrate such as grains or starchy vegetables, and one-half non-starchy vegetables.

Educate Yourself and Learn to Compromise

In addition to understanding the food guides, it can be helpful to read a reference book or two to learn the caloric content and nutritional value of various foods. Then you will be armed with the information you need to be an educated consumer of great foods. You will know what to look for on the labels of the foods you buy (more on food labels below). You will understand which fruits and vegetables provide the most nutrients. It will be easy to make the right food choices for you and your family, enabling you to eat a wide variety of delicious, eye-appealing foods and to live the high-energy, vital lives you deserve. What could be more empowering than that?

I don't want you to think that eating healthfully is all work and no fun. It's not about deprivation; as I said earlier, I believe in moderation. There is room in your diet for every kind of food. If you really want a chocolate bar, eat it, but just half. Or upgrade the quality of the chocolate, so that when you do indulge, it is a real treat. Research shows that dark chocolate consisting of 70 percent or more cocoa contains beneficial amounts of bioflavonoids, thought to have heart-healthy antioxidant qualities. Milk chocolate or less pure chocolate that has more sugar and other added ingredients is not as beneficial. Whenever I need my chocolate fix, I take a square of a 70 percent cocoa-based chocolate bar and let it melt in my mouth instead of biting and eating it quickly. Try it— you'll be surprised at the lasting satisfaction.

If you're like me and love to occasionally indulge in french fries, choose the best-quality fries you can find at the supermarket—those without trans fats—or enjoy a small portion at the fast-food outlet. Just don't eat a huge quantity. About twenty oven-baked fries have less fat than a pat of butter or margarine. And this amount compares favourably with many other popular starch choices—seasoned rice, boil-in-a-bag converted rice, or a side order of pasta—in terms of calories, fat, protein, and carbs. Potatoes are a misunderstood vegetable. Did you know that a potato contains carbohydrates, vitamin C, B vitamins, potassium, magnesium, phosphorus, iron, and fibre if eaten with the skin on? To keep potatoes interesting, vary the way you prepare them. For instance, you might try a baked potato with low-fat sour cream; a boiled new potato with fresh dill, a small pat of butter, and salt and pepper; or my baked Potato Wedge Fries (see page 179 for the recipe), which is one of my family's favourites.

Once you are comfortable with types of foods and portions, you will be more likely to select healthy alternatives from restaurant menus (don't be shy about asking how things are prepared).

Food Labels

Choosing healthy foods when grocery shopping can be a humbling experience. We all know that we should be reading the food labels, but how many of us are label savvy? Most of us don't know what to look for on the nutrition label. We are often easily swayed by a product's claims. Never make a food choice based on a product label. It is important to read between the lines and know what marketing terms really mean. A food can be "light," "low in cholesterol," and contain "no fat," yet still be loaded with calories.

Recent laws in Canada made it mandatory for large food manufacturers to include on the packaging of all their products a label listing major nutrition components; small manufacturers are required to do so by December 2007. The nutrients listed on the food label are in grams and milligrams and also appear as a percentage of the total recommended daily intake (RDI) for someone consuming 2000 calories daily. If you eat more or less calories, you'll need to make the appropriate adjustments.

Meal Planning

I am a big believer that planning is essential to success, and this means getting organized. Planning your meals allows you to shop for the ingredients in advance, having them on hand for when you are ready to cook—you'll be ready to make a healthy and delicious dinner as soon as you walk in the door after work. If your focus is losing weight, it makes even more sense to take the time to plan your meals well in advance and have your kitchen stocked with the groceries you'll need. Planning allows you to factor in the calories of each day's meal plan. (And remember, once your healthy body weight has been attained, calories in must equal calories out in order to maintain that healthy body weight.) If you don't leave yourself enough time to prepare and eat, say, a healthy breakfast, it won't be long before you're back at a fast-food outlet grabbing a doughnut and coffee for a mid-morning snack or a burger and milkshake for lunch. Consider brown-bagging your lunch to work if you don't already. You will have much more control over ingredients and quantity if you prepare the lunch yourself.

Choose the foods you enjoy when planning your meals. Don't deprive yourself of any one food. Eat everything you enjoy in moderation—be sure to read the food label so you know the serving size. And don't force yourself to eat foods you don't like just because they are healthful.

I've included a one-week healthy eating plan at the end of this chapter (see page 68), as well as 25 healthy recipes at the back of this book to get you started. Plan your meals weekly, daily, or whatever best suits your schedule. Remember to keep your meals well balanced with a combination of food from all the food groups. Then make a list of the groceries you'll need for your meal plan. Consider ordering online and having your groceries delivered to save time.

If you do need to whip up a meal on the spur of the moment, one of the best ways to ensure you are able to prepare a healthy and delicious one is by keeping your pantry stocked with the

PANTRY ITEMS

Basil

Black pepper

Cinnamon

Dill

Ground ginger

Oregano

Paprika

Pepper, cayenne, dried flakes

Poppy seeds

Rosemary

Sea salt

Sesame seeds

Thyme

Turmeric

BAKING INGREDIENTS

Baking powder

Baking soda

Chocolate chips, semi-sweet

Cocoa, unsweetened

Cookie crumbs

Cornstarch

Flour, white and whole wheat

Sugar, white and brown

Vanilla extract

CANNED GOODS

Beans and legumes

Corn niblets

Evaporated milk

Mandarin oranges

Olives, sliced, in water

Tomato paste

Tomatoes, whole or crushed

Tuna, water-packed

OILS AND VINEGARS

Canola oil

Olive oil

Vegetable spray

Vinegar—balsamic, red wine, cider, and rice

CONDIMENTS

Barbecue sauce

Dijon mustard

Ketchup

Mayonnaise, light

Peanut butter, natural

Roasted red bell peppers packed in water

Salad dressings, low-fat

Salsa

REFRIGERATED OR FROZEN ITEMS

Butter or margarine

Cheeses: Parmesan, light feta, cream, cheddar, ricotta, and goat

Corn and peas, frozen

Eggs, whole, natural egg substitute

Fruits and vegetables (fresh)

Fruits and berries, frozen, without sugar

Meat, frozen, organic if possible

Milk—2% milk fat or lower

Orange juice, frozen concentrate

Sour cream, low-fat

Tofu, firm and soft

Yogourt, low-fat

various dry, refrigerated, and frozen goods you need to augment and flavour your fresh grocery items. You can even make ethnic pantries—Italian, Asian, Mexican, and Indian. The chart on page 62 lists some of the items I always have on hand.

Some cheese—Parmesan, cheddar, mozzarella, and Swiss—is freezable, but only if it will be used for cooking.

Frozen fruits and vegetables usually contain as many or more nutrients than their fresh supermarket counterparts because they are flash-frozen immediately after being picked. Fresh produce often takes several days—sometimes even as long as two weeks—to arrive at the supermarket, meaning the time between picking and eating is much longer. The longer that time delay, the greater the loss of nutrients from the produce.

Meats that freeze well include lean ground beef, pork, chicken, or turkey; boneless chicken breasts and thighs; chicken breasts with bones; whole chickens; lean steaks including rib-eye, tenderloin, flank, and sirloin; beef, veal, or pork tenderloin roasts; stewing beef, and raw shrimp. To avoid freezer burn of your meats, don't store them for too long in the freezer. Packaging must be moisture- and vapour-proof: Wrap items carefully with freezer plastic bags, heavy aluminum foil, or polyethylene-lined paper.

Nuts, dried fruits, sun-dried tomatoes, and grains can all be kept in the freezer as well.

Substitutions

To start cooking and eating more healthfully, you'll need to know which low-fat foods can be substituted for high-fat ones. Page 64 lists just a few.

If, like me, you like to indulge in a rich dessert on occasion, bake your own, substituting as much as 75 percent of the butter or oil with low-fat yogourt, sour cream, puréed ripe banana, crushed pineapple, grated carrots, cooked mashed dates, or applesauce. For example, if a recipe calls for 1 cup of butter or oil, you could use 1/4 cup of oil and 3/4 cup of any of the above ingredients (depending on the flavour of the dessert). See my dessert recipes on pages 187 and 188 for those that have been perfectly tested.

What Is Sabotaging You?

For those of you who have used food in the past for comfort (as well as for healthy fuel), pay close attention to how you deal with emotional ups and downs. As you shift your focus to healthy eating, old negative and sabotaging habits can easily derail your best efforts. Don't think of your new eating routine as going on or off a diet. It's about lifestyle and finding a new comfort zone. Watch when the old habits start to creep back into your life. For instance, you may find yourself starting to eat later in the evening again, or going for many hours without food. Get yourself back in line quickly. Always have healthy snacks available. When you have certain cravings or are in a mood that requires comfort food, indulge with moderation and control. Remind yourself every day why you're eating well.

I encourage you all to take charge of your wellness. Most of us would like to live long and healthy lives, and dramatically decrease our risk of disease. There is no age at which it is too late to start on this path. And, as you begin this process of changing your eating habits to bring balance to your life, remember to stick with small steps—doing One Thing Right each day will get you to where you want to be. Including a healthy selection from each of the food groups in every meal is a terrific example of doing One Thing Right.

The progress I've made on my own journey toward wellness, coupled with my enthusiasm, has been infectious. My system has worked so well for me that others—both family and friends—have been inspired to join me.

Feeding a family healthy food is not always easy. At one time or another, many parents I know have had a child with a weight issue. In my experience, expecting adolescents to listen to common sense from their parent, let alone getting them to eat foods they say they don't want, is well-nigh impossible. But don't be discouraged. Start by addressing the problem in

High Fat	Lower Fat
heavy cream	2% evaporated milk
regular mayonnaise	light mayonnaise (50% less fat)
regular sour cream	low-fat sour cream or yogourt
chocolate	cocoa as directed in recipe
butter	non-hydrogenated margarine, or canola or grapeseed oil
ice cream	frozen yogourt or sorbet
full-fat cheese	lower fat varieties such as goat or feta
regular salad dressings	low-fat dressings
eggs	egg whites or a natural egg substitute
potato chips	baked potato or tortilla chips, pretzels

small ways. Instead of having cookies for snacks in the ravenous after-school hour, leave a plate on the kitchen counter piled with cut fruit and vegetables. I don't believe in forcing children to eat anything. I simply ask them to try a couple of mouthfuls of everything I prepare. If they like it, great; if they don't, they don't have to eat any more. And I listen to them and try to provide foods they do like—but in a healthier version if it's a type of fast food or snack food. For children—indeed, for everyone—eating healthfully is half the battle of wellness. Regular activity is the other half. And starting children on the right path with each of these

building blocks early in their lives puts them on the road to a balanced, healthy life.

So now what? Start slowly, but please start. It would make me happy to hear that someone who had a doughnut and coffee every morning began to have that doughnut only every other morning. That's real progress and it's a first building block. Another small step is to include cooked or raw fruits and vegetables in each meal—you can't beat them for nutrients. I believe that small steps and moderation are the best way to succeed in creating balance with food in the wellness of your life. You will find that life never tasted—and felt—so good.

"Take charge of your wellness. There is no age at which it is too late to start on this path. Remember to stick with small steps—doing one thing right each day will get you to where you want to be."

my food journal

When calculating your total foods for each day, check the guidelines below for quantities of specific foods. The larger serving sizes are meant for those who are physically active. For example, if you have a sedentary lifestyle, you should have 5 grains per day; if you exercise daily at a vigorous level, you should have 12 grains.

Grains: 5–12 servings per day
One serving = 1 slice toast; 3/4 cup cereal; 1/2 small bagel, pita, or bun; 1 cup pasta or rice

Fruits and vegetables: 5–10 servings per day
One serving = 1 medium-sized fruit or vegetable; 1/2 cup canned or frozen vegetables or fruit; 1 cup green salad; 1/2 cup juice

Meat and alternatives: 3–4 servings per day
One serving = 3 oz chicken, beef, or fish; 1/2 cup beans; (1–2 eggs) 2 tablespoons peanut butter

Dairy products: 2–3 servings per day
One serving = 2 slices packaged cheese; 3/4 cup yogourt; 1 cup low-fat milk

Fats/sugars: keep to a minimum
(e.g., butter, oil, sugar, jam, desserts)

week 1

MONDAY

Total proteins: _____

Total breads/grains: _____

Total fruits/vegetables: _____

Total dairy: _____

Total water: _____

Total beverages (other than water): _____

Total fats and sugars: _____

Day's exercise, including duration:

_____

_____

_____

_____

_____

Stress level (rate on a scale of 0 to 5): _____

Day's comments:

_____

_____

_____

_____

_____

_____

_____

Weekly weight: _____

Total proteins: _____

Total breads/grains: _____

Total fruits/vegetables: _____

Total dairy: _____

Total water: _____

Total beverages (other than water): _____

Total fats and sugars: _____

Day's exercise, including duration:

_____

_____

_____

_____

_____

Stress level (rate on a scale of 0 to 5): _____

Day's comments:

_____

_____

_____

_____

_____

_____

_____

Weekly weight: _____

Total proteins: _____

Total breads/grains: _____

Total fruits/vegetables: _____

Total dairy: _____

Total water: _____

Total beverages (other than water): _____

Total fats and sugars: _____

Day's exercise, including duration:

_____

_____

_____

_____

_____

Stress level (rate on a scale of 0 to 5): _____

Day's comments:

_____

_____

_____

_____

_____

_____

_____

Weekly weight: _____

THURSDAY

Total proteins: _____

Total breads/grains: _____

Total fruits/vegetables: _____

Total dairy: _____

Total water: _____

Total beverages (other than water): _____

Total fats and sugars: _____

Day's exercise, including duration:

_____

_____

_____

_____

Stress level (rate on a scale of 0 to 5): _____

Day's comments:

_____

_____

_____

_____

_____

_____

_____

Weekly weight: _____

FRIDAY

Total proteins: _____

Total breads/grains: _____

Total fruits/vegetables: _____

Total dairy: _____

Total water: _____

Total beverages (other than water): _____

Total fats and sugars: _____

Day's exercise, including duration:

_____

_____

_____

_____

Stress level (rate on a scale of 0 to 5): _____

Day's comments:

_____

_____

_____

_____

_____

_____

_____

Weekly weight: _____

SATURDAY

Total proteins: _____

Total breads/grains: _____

Total fruits/vegetables: _____

Total dairy: _____

Total water: _____

Total beverages (other than water): _____

Total fats and sugars: _____

Day's exercise, including duration:

_____

_____

_____

_____

_____

Stress level (rate on a scale of 0 to 5): _____

Day's comments:

_____

_____

_____

_____

_____

_____

Weekly weight: _____

SUNDAY

Total proteins: _____

Total breads/grains: _____

Total fruits/vegetables: _____

Total dairy: _____

Total water: _____

Total beverages (other than water): _____

Total fats and sugars: _____

Day's exercise, including duration:

_____

_____

_____

_____

_____

Stress level (rate on a scale of 0 to 5): _____

Day's comments:

_____

_____

_____

_____

_____

_____

Weekly weight: _____

one-week healthy eating plan

monday

BREAKFAST	CALORIES
1/2 whole-wheat bagel	100
1/3 cup scrambled egg substitute, pan sprayed with vegetable spray	60
1 medium fruit	80

SNACK	
1/2 cup low-fat, sugar-free yogourt	50

LUNCH	
1 large whole-wheat pita	170
3 oz sliced roasted turkey or chicken	140
tomatoes, lettuce, onions, Dijon mustard	20
1 medium fruit	80

SNACK	
small low-fat latte	100

DINNER	
6 oz grilled salmon with 2 tbsp teriyaki sauce	350
3 cups grilled vegetables, using vegetable spray	100
1/2 cup brown rice	100
1 1/2 cups cubed fresh pineapple	100

SNACK	
1/2 cup low-fat frozen yogourt or ice cream	100
TOTAL	**1550**

tuesday

BREAKFAST	CALORIES
1/3 cup egg-white omelette with 1 oz goat or feta cheese	110
1 slice whole-wheat toast	70
1 orange	80

SNACK	
1/2 cup low-fat cottage cheese	80
2 large whole-wheat crackers	40

LUNCH	
2 cups tossed salad with 2 tbsp low-fat dressing	100
4 oz grilled chicken	170
1 small apple	60

SNACK	
small low-fat latte	100

DINNER	
4 oz beef stir-fry with 3 cups vegetables, 3 tbsp teriyaki sauce	400
1/2 cup brown rice	100
2 cups diced watermelon	100

SNACK	
20 pistachios	85
TOTAL	**1495**

wednesday

BREAKFAST	CALORIES
1 oz high-fibre cereal with 1/4 cup low-fat milk	125
1 medium banana	100

SNACK	
1 oz low-fat cheese stick	80
2 large whole-wheat crackers	40

LUNCH	
3 oz water-packed tuna with 2 tbsp low-fat mayonnaise on 2 oz whole-wheat roll	400
1 medium apple	80

SNACK	
1/2 cup low-fat, sugar-free yogourt	50

DINNER	
8 large grilled shrimp	100
1/4 cup cocktail sauce	30
1 small cob of corn	80
3 cups grilled vegetables, using vegetable spray	100
1 1/2 cups sliced strawberries	75

SNACK	
2 cups microwave light popcorn	60
TOTAL	**1320**

thursday

BREAKFAST	CALORIES
1/2 cup oatmeal with	
1/2 cup low-fat milk	135
1/4 cup cantaloupe	75
1/4 cup raisins	124

SNACK	
1 medium fruit	80

LUNCH	
1 cup chicken vegetable soup	90
3 oz vegetarian burger	140
1 whole-wheat bun	100
lettuce and tomato garnish	20

SNACK	
15 almonds	100

DINNER	
4 oz grilled tuna or swordfish	
with 2 tbsp bottled Asian dressing	150
3 cups grilled vegetables,	
using vegetable spray	100
1/2 cup brown rice	100

SNACK	
1 cup grapes	100
TOTAL	**1314**

friday

BREAKFAST	CALORIES
1 whole-wheat toasted	
English muffin with 2 tbsp	
low-fat peanut butter	235
1 medium apple	70

SNACK	
1 low-fat cheese stick	80
6 slices Melba toast	100

LUNCH	
1 cup vegetable tomato soup	150
1/2 cup chopped surimi (imitation	
crabmeat) with 1 cup diced	
vegetables, 2 tbsp low-fat mayonnaise	175

SNACK	
1/2 cup low-fat, sugar-free yogourt	50
10 dried apricots	80

DINNER	
2 oz dry pasta (approximately 2 cups	
cooked) with 1/2 cup tomato sauce	
and 2 tbsp grated Parmesan cheese	300
4 oz grilled chicken	170

SNACK	
2 cups microwave light popcorn	60
TOTAL	**1470**

saturday

BREAKFAST	CALORIES
1/3 cup scrambled egg substitute, pan sprayed with vegetable spray	60
1 slice whole-wheat toast	70
1 medium orange	80

SNACK	
small low-fat latte	100

LUNCH	
1 8-inch whole-wheat tortilla with 3 oz water-packed tuna, 2 tbsp low-fat mayonnaise, tomatoes and lettuce	330
1 1/2 cups strawberries	75

SNACK	
2 tbsp hummus	50
1/2 cup each sliced celery and carrots	50

DINNER	
1 cup clear chicken vegetable soup, or 2 cups miso soup	80
4 oz stir-fried firm tofu (marinated in teriyaki sauce) with 3 cups vegetables sautéed using vegetable spray, 1 cup brown rice	370

SNACK	
1/2 cup low-fat frozen yogourt or ice cream	100
TOTAL	**1365**

sunday

BREAKFAST	CALORIES
1 oz high-fibre cereal with 1/4 cup low-fat milk	125
1 medium banana	80

SNACK	
1/4 cup dried fruit	100

LUNCH	
3 oz grilled chicken breast	120
1 whole-wheat bun	110
lettuce and tomato garnish	20

SNACK	
1 cup fruit smoothie made with low-fat milk or yogourt	100

DINNER	
1 cup vegetarian chili	300
1 small baked potato	150
2 cups tossed salad with 2 tbsp low-fat dressing	100

SNACK	
1 tbsp low-fat peanut butter	60
1 small apple, sliced	60
TOTAL	**1325**

family
growing
together

family growing together

Taking on the roles of nurturer, organizer, homework monitor, disciplinarian, psychologist, caterer, spouse, laundress, and transportation co-coordinator for a husband, four kids, and four pets is exhausting. In other words, I'm a typical mother. It's a very time- and energy-consuming job.

Family is one of the greatest priorities in my life, and I therefore devote a large amount of my time and energy to it. It can be a challenge balancing all the areas of my life in a way that works for me. Family is one of the most important segments of my wheel of life, since it directly affects the other segments. For instance, many of my friends are associated with my family. How I look at food is in response to my family's requests. My fashion statement has to be in line with my family's life, and our financial situation is affected by my family life. Like most of us, on any given day if my husband or my child needs me, I have to postpone other activities I had planned until the family issue is resolved. Although being a mother is a juggling act that is far from easy, I'm sure that most of us wouldn't have it any other way.

To ensure a well-functioning family life, you need to take on the role of focusing and leading the family and enforcing your beliefs and values. You become the role model for what's acceptable and what's not. What your children learn in their home life will shape their views and accomplishments in life.

I meet a lot of stressed-out women (along with their stressed-out husbands) in my travels. Certainly, it shouldn't surprise us that everyone's so stressed. People today have a lot more on their plates than they used to. In many households, both parents work full time, raise children, have mortgages and bills to pay, coach soccer or volunteer in the community, and try to maintain social and personal lives as well. Because none of us wants to let anyone down or break commitments, the time and performance

"To say that one style of parenting is right for everyone is like saying that we should all eat only one kind of food."

demands are often overwhelming. But I think we've all realized that we want and need to think about the balance between all the important elements in our lives.

Of life's various elements, few priorities rank as high as family for many of us. People set such high standards for and have such commitment to their families that the other parts of their lives often get neglected. A lot of the questions people ask me in the course of my work have to do with maintaining a sense of self in spite of the strong pull of family—questions such as, how do I find the time to meet the demands of my family, and in some cases career as well, and still be me? How do I get it all done and still find the time to prioritize my own health and wellness?

These were certainly issues that I considered when I thought about getting married and having children, and that I have continually had to deal with since having a family. Somewhere along the way, I learned that I had to maintain time and energy for my own priorities, in balance with all the other people and things that mattered to me.

We all operate with different guidelines and principles. As anyone who has ever purchased

pantyhose will tell you, one size does *not* fit all. And that's the point of this exercise: to find a flexible and easy-to-implement way to integrate change into your own individual formula, whatever the category—family, fitness, fashion, or even fun. To say that one style of parenting is right for everyone is like saying that we should all eat only one kind of food.

In the family part of my life, with my husband, four kids, and four pets, I go through my formula for change at hyper-speed compared to the other segments of my life. I check in on *where am I now?*—which is A—and also on *where do I want to be?*—which is B—on a daily basis. And I keep track of where my children and husband are and want to be each day as well. We mothers always think we need to help out with everything. Following my own individual recipe, or formula, is in part how I get from A to B.

Life's Directions

We have all made decisions along the way that have had a great impact on our family life. They might go as far back as your school days, when you took a special interest in a certain subject or extracurricular activity. These interests may have led you to your chosen career. Or perhaps the person you married dictated your future, or the different personalities of your children led you in a specific direction. In my life there have been three pivotal life decisions or turning points. I didn't always have the system for dealing with change that I do now. But I did always analyze my options carefully and tried to keep in mind my long-term objectives when I made big decisions. For me, those big moments were—

1. Marrying the sort of man who balances my personality and who I know brings out the best in me, and I in him.
2. Having my four children and learning how to keep our life in balance while living with so many different personalities.
3. Attempting to develop and maintain a satisfying career while raising a family.

Although I did give great consideration to these decisions, ultimately I went with my instincts of what I felt was right. I knew that I didn't want to look back and say that I should have done things differently.

Your Partner

We all need to love and be loved. It's human nature. We all want to have a relationship that is successful, loving, productive, long lasting, and supportive. Selecting the right partner for life is no easy task and definitely has no guarantees. Statistics show that one in two marriages in North America end in divorce. Often we find that the person we fell in love with years ago has grown into someone else. Or it may be you who has grown and changed over the years. You have two choices: to work with what you have to develop a mutual love and respect, or to realize that both of you have drifted too far apart to salvage the relationship. Of course, hopefully you are able to work with who you both are and enrich the relationship for each other and your family. But if the two of you have drifted too far apart, take what you have learned from the relationship and apply it to a new and more enriching relationship.

The courage to look at yourself and make the necessary changes will inspire those around you.

where am I now?

What three important points in my life helped mould who I am today?

1. _____
_____
_____
_____
_____
_____

2. _____
_____
_____
_____
_____
_____

3. _____
_____
_____
_____
_____
_____

Am I happy with myself?   ☐ Yes   ☐ No

where do I want to be?

If I am not happy with myself, what changes would I like to make? Or, even if I am happy with myself, what changes would I still like to implement?

1. _____
   _____
   _____
   _____

2. _____
   _____
   _____
   _____

3. _____
   _____
   _____
   _____

It's easy to blame others for your inadequacies and weaknesses. But in the end you are responsible for yourself and your happiness. You can't continue blaming others. You have to be willing to see where improvements can be made to enrich your life. There has to be a willingness to own your own problems. The courage to look at yourself and make the necessary changes will inspire those around you.

where am I now?

How many years have I been with my partner?

_____

_____

_____

Of our years together, how many have been
rewarding and loving? _____

_____

_____

_____

Do I feel that my opinions and thoughts are
respected even if they are different from my
partner's?   ☐ Yes   ☐ No

Do we give each other the space and independ-
ence we need?   ☐ Yes   ☐ No

When we argue, are we keeping the discussion
in control or are we getting angry and always
raising our voices?   ☐ Yes   ☐ No

Do we clear the air immediately and discuss our
differences after a disagreement, or do we go for
hours or even days without speaking?
                              ☐ Yes   ☐ No

Even if I believe I'm right, am I able to say I'm
sorry if my partner can't?   ☐ Yes   ☐ No

Do we respect each other's privacy?
                              ☐ Yes   ☐ No

Chances are that if you answered yes to most of the above questions, you understand your partner's needs and have similar values. If you answered no to more than one question, there may be tension in the relationship that will ultimately affect your family life. Asking yourself these next questions might help you understand what's going on in your relationship and allow you to set up a more productive direction to work toward.

When did the years together become more burdensome and why? _____

_____

_____

_____

_____

_____

Why do I think my opinions aren't being respected? _____

_____

_____

_____

_____

_____

_____

What happened in my partner's life to change the way he or she reacts to me?

_____

_____

_____

_____

_____

If I've become more demanding or needy and less independent over the years, what caused that change? _____

_____

_____

_____

_____

_____

Why does a disagreement make me so angry and not allow me to make peace in a positive manner?

_____

_____

_____

_____

where do I want to be?

Do I want to communicate on an equal ground with my partner? ☐ Yes ☐ No

Do I want to have unconditional support and love? ☐ Yes ☐ No

Do I want to be accepted for who I am? ☐ Yes ☐ No

Do I want to spend more quality time with my partner? ☐ Yes ☐ No

I'm certain that the answers to the above are all yes. So how do you get from here to there? There's no question that my husband and I have had our ups and downs, but he has also become my best friend over the years. We support each other and never intentionally try to hurt each other. Working together as a partnership has allowed us to reap the benefits of a healthy married life and enjoy the fruits of our labour, namely our children. Here are the major guidelines I follow in my now thirty-year marriage:

- I realize that both my husband and I are two distinct individuals. Even if we share common values and goals, we still think differently. That means we have to try to understand the other person's point of view, no matter how different it is from ours.

- After that first rush of passion and romance, the partnership becomes one of commitment and unconditional love. My husband has to be there for the good times and for the not so good times, and so do I.

- Disagreements are normal and healthy for the relationship. I don't let them ever threaten the partnership. I try to be civil and won't get into a screaming match—yelling only antagonizes the other person.

- I realize that I don't have to be right all the time. Admitting you're wrong is difficult for many people. But I've found that saying you're sorry and apologizing can be humbling and refreshing. And timing can be so crucial. Often I walk away from a heated discussion when I realize our different points of view are not going to get solved at that moment. I let my husband have his own space for a while. Often it doesn't take long for him to see where I am coming from, and vice versa, and then we can talk about it. If we had continued on the path of an all out fight, we both would have lost.

- I realize that I can't always be in control of all family situations. I know I can't always have my own way.

- I set a date with my husband for at least once a week, to be in a space where we're alone without the kids and without friends and can talk for at least two hours. It can't be a movie. A walk or dinner is perfect.

- I listen to what my husband is saying, no matter whether he is talking about family, friends, work, or some other topic. I always try to give my undivided attention.

- I confront problems on a regular basis. Burying issues only develops resentment and anger. A relationship problem may never be completely solved, but it can be managed so that it causes less stress.

- At any opportunity, I try to bolster my husband's self-esteem in an honest and sincere way.

- I strive to meet my husband's emotional, social, and spiritual needs.

The Family Mosaic

Even with my and my husband's techniques for managing issues as a couple, life is not problem-free. Four children later, we still struggle. Sure, it's great to cuddle and play with an adorable baby. But then there are the sleepless nights, irrational moods, and largest responsibility you could ever have. And when your children get older, each one with their individual emotional ups and downs, it can be tough. It can be difficult, time-consuming, and emotionally draining to deal with each child's issues, and you may often disagree with your spouse on which course of action to take. My husband and I have occasionally needed to seek the advice of a professional counsellor to help us sort through our disagreements and various issues. In the end we always come together to be united in front of the children. Parenting never stops being a lot of work, but it is worth it.

The greatest fear I had about having children was that, by spending more time raising my children than focusing on my career, I would lose my identity. How would I successfully combine motherhood and career and all the other important things in my life? I knew I was hardly the first woman to face these issues. I was determined to design my life in a way that would really work for me—to find a balance and to follow my own system.

My One Thing Right in my plan was to keep my own identity a priority when planning for motherhood. I knew that was the key to success for me. I knew my husband would be supportive of any career I had that combined well with family, and I decided to embark on my new career in food while at home raising my four children.

Raising children and trying to have a solid family life is definitely challenging, but over time we have learned to break each problem down into manageable, smaller pieces. We make progress toward objectives one small step at a time, which is the philosophy I use to balance the six Fs in my wheel of life.

You and Your Children

Everyone's children are originals, each with their own talents and challenges. Each child develops in his or her own way. In my case, parenting four children does not involve one parenting approach. It would be easier if it did, but each child is different and requires a unique approach.

But one thing I *have* had to do for all four of my children was learn to take a step back as they've gotten older and to allow them to design their lives for themselves. This may have been one of the toughest things ever. We all know how tempting it is to try to solve our children's problems for them—to impose our recipe for life on them. What we really need to do is teach them how to create their own building blocks and their own frameworks so they'll know how to survive in the world. One of the ways to do this is by letting them make their own mistakes. I know this is easier said than done. When my oldest two children were ready to leave for university, I felt sad and lonely. My husband, on the other hand, was thrilled to see them starting on this phase of their lives. I'll never forget his words: "What's worse—seeing your children go off to start their own lives, or having them stay with you forever?" I think about this every time they leave me for school, work, or summer holidays.

Children need to be confident and competent in what they do day to day. They need unconditional love, acceptance, support, structure, and guiding rules, and a solid home foundation and freedom from guilt or blame should the parents separate or divorce. This is a tall order for parents, especially single parents.

"We all know how tempting it is to try to solve our children's problems for them—to impose our recipe for life on them. What we really need to do is teach them how to create their own building blocks."

where am I now?

The following questions are designed to help you determine how you and your children interact.

Do I at times show preference to one of my children? ☐ Yes ☐ No

Is there often tension between various siblings and me and my partner? ☐ Yes ☐ No

Do any of my children have poor self-esteem? ☐ Yes ☐ No

Do I discipline all the children the same? ☐ Yes ☐ No

Does the family often go for days without sitting down to a meal together? ☐ Yes ☐ No

Am I often unaware of my teen's whereabouts? ☐ Yes ☐ No

Am I often unaware of what work my child is doing at school? ☐ Yes ☐ No

Do I and my partner often disagree about how to discipline the children? ☐ Yes ☐ No

Do my children often go to their rooms and stay there for hours either on the computer or telephone, or listening to music? ☐ Yes ☐ No

When a crisis hits, do I usually envision catastrophic ramifications? ☐ Yes ☐ No

If you answered yes to more than three of these questions, you might want to take a closer look at the dynamics of your family and how you all relate. Do you all enjoy being at home, or is it a place of stress and anxiety? Do you have open communication, or does everyone keep to themselves?

where do I want to be?

Do I want to have a healthy long-term relationship with my children? ☐ Yes ☐ No

Do I want them to be self-reliant, independent, and emotionally stable adults? ☐ Yes ☐ No

Do I want to do more activities with them? ☐ Yes ☐ No

Do I want to have honest and direct conversations with them? ☐ Yes ☐ No

Do I want them to know my weaknesses as well as my strengths? ☐ Yes ☐ No

Do I want to always be seen as supporting their endeavours rather than criticizing them? ☐ Yes ☐ No

I'm guessing that your answers to the *where do I want to be* questions are yes. We all want a well-functioning, happy home life with our children. Too often, though, in parenting we rely on the methods our parents used to raise us, which may not be suitable for our own children, or we rely on ineffective behaviours that often have a negative impact. For instance, bullying or bribing children into making particular choices may only turn them into bullies themselves. Remember, you always need to be the role model: You can't tell your children to live a certain way when you're doing the opposite. Yet, the common mistakes we often make in a family are not easy to avoid, since patterns develop over years, but to change the dynamics of the family, change has to happen.

Here are some of the practices and principles my husband and I have followed over the years in raising our four children. Remember, we've had four to experiment with. It's often trial and error, and you tend to get more experienced with each one. But what works for one may not work for another: There is no clear-cut formula. But I think our general guidelines are helpful:

● We recognize that children need boundaries. We try to be clear about what we expect in terms of behaviour and have a civil discussion when the boundaries are being questioned and tested.

● When a problem with one of our children arises, my husband and I decide which of us will deal with it. We have found that inevitably one of us is better equipped to handle the particular situation. For example, perhaps one of us feels he or she will put the child on the defensive. So that person steps aside for a while. This way, we avoid escalating conflict and our message gets through to our child.

● We try not to solve our children's issues and problems for them, but rather discuss *with* them how the problem might be resolved.

● We continually assess to determine where we are. We determine, with the children's help, where they each want to be, and we figure out

a proactive plan to get them there. The children appreciate the inclusive approach and this makes them participate all the more. We make sure the action plan is made up of small steps so that it doesn't seem overwhelming. Focusing on getting One Thing Right takes a lot of the pressure off the children, and they are more likely to feel a sense of achievement when the goals are manageable. Each time a problem is solved or an objective reached, our kids feel like they've created a solid building block in the design of their own lives. They love the feeling of progress.

● We make our home environment a place where our children can express their views and they know they are emotionally accepted no matter what.

● We reschedule our work and social activities to spend time with the children and as a family. We always take at least one family holiday a year without friends or extended family members.

● We remind ourselves that each child is different and that what we want that child to be is not important or useful. They all need to be given opportunities to self-actualize, and we must respect their different approaches— not always easy when their opinions don't coincide with our own.

- We try not to criticize our children when they do something wrong. Instead, we try to compliment when they do something right.

- We strive to create a stable home, even if my husband and I aren't seeing eye to eye about something or are going through personal difficulty. Parenting together is crucial so kids don't play one of you off against the other.

- We try to establish rituals that the kids are a part of, so that we are all reminded that we are a family. It might be having dinner together on a certain night of the week. (Check out my recipes on page 163 that the entire family can enjoy and which will help teach kids about healthy eating.) Or spending an annual holiday together—just the immediate family, and no friends.

- We always aim for effective communication. This can be a challenge: It is easy to interrogate our kids in an effort to find out what's going on in their lives. But this can lead to distrust rather than open and honest communication. Instead, we try to talk to them—even about the small details in their lives—with the objective of understanding, and to respond in a non-judgmental way. We try to listen to what our children have to say, including their concerns and complaints, and avoid a know-it-all attitude. Our children definitely have

important things to tell us, so we let them talk, no matter how they may sound.

- When a crisis occurs, we try to stay calm and not immediately lay blame. Our staying in control gives our children confidence and reassurance. Otherwise they are left feeling insecure, anxious, and alone.

- We try not to repeat any negative learned behaviours we grew up with. Our past is not our future.

- We strive to stop worrying about tomorrow and focus on today, no matter how large a problem may seem. If we are always asking, what if?, we become anxious and it is easy to fall into patterns of catastrophic thinking.

- We always keep in mind that our family can determine what we become in life and how we think of ourselves.

I don't always find it easy to always follow the principles I've laid out for myself, especially when I'm pressed for time. And, like most women I meet, the demands on my time seem to increase every year. I find that in order to fit it all in, aside from being an organized multi-tasker—something I definitely had to learn—I have to be flexible. I must be able to shift my priorities from one child to another at a moment's notice. And I need to be able to shift my focus from work to family to fitness and food and back again to family just as fast.

I've accepted that I can't do as much in a day as I might want. This doesn't mean I'm not incredibly busy—I am. But once I made the choice to have four children, I knew that I wouldn't be able to do everything I wanted, especially when the children were young. And I couldn't do as many activities with friends or go shopping as often, or pursue as many hobbies as I might have if I'd had fewer children. But I made an informed choice that I'm happy with. Other choices would have meant different priorities and time allocations, and that would have been fine too—this is the point I made earlier about each person needing to create her or his own model for balance. And as the children are growing older and more independent, the various areas of life are finding a different balance.

The Family Journal

One of the ways I evaluate how things are going in my family is by asking myself whether I have a sense of peace and control, or whether I'm feeling anxious and out of control. I think of it as a family journal that helps identify areas I want to work on with my family. I ask myself, where in the family do I not feel at peace? Is there a specific family person with whom there is more stress? Once I have identified the issue or the person, I ask myself, what can I do about it?

I believe that we can do something about almost anything. If I'm working on an issue, I feel productive and I sense I'm making a difference. A family journal works for family in much the same way as a food journal works for food. If you keep a diary for 2 weeks, noting where in your family you do and don't feel at peace, as well as how you spent your time, you'll likely notice some patterns. You might see where you can make small changes by doing One Thing Right, which could translate into big results in your family life. I encourage you to keep a family journal on an ongoing basis, evaluating it on a weekly basis. I've included a sample family journal at the end of this chapter (see page 94).

Let me give you two examples of how a family journal can be helpful, just in terms of time management. A few years ago, when reviewing the family journal I was keeping, I noticed that I was continually late. I was having trouble juggling my schedule to accommodate everyone. So I decided to get a BlackBerry. Many people think BlackBerrys are for big-business types only. But, as most of parents know, when you need to keep track of the kids' lessons, soccer games, car-pooling, and your own to-do lists and appointments, you've got just as hectic a pace as any CEO. You manage your own company … it's called your family.

When a friend of mine reviewed her family journal, she noted that it took her 40 minutes to get home from the office every night because of the heavy rush-hour traffic. This is something

> "Create a system that works for your life—that's the balance of living well."

she already knew. But it was by looking at her journal and seeing this pattern in black and white that it dawned on her that if she stayed an extra 20 productive minutes at the office each night, she saved herself 20 minutes of sitting in traffic because she missed the worst of the rush. That freed up 20 minutes at lunchtime to work out, which meant she didn't have to work out in the morning. She spent the 20 extra minutes having breakfast with her daughter instead.

BECAUSE I CHOSE to be a mother to four children, a lot of my time and energy until now has gone into my family. It represents a large portion of my life. That was the way I designed it, and it works for me. My years as a mother have forced me to change and grow a great deal, and they've brought my husband and me closer together. I've learned to maintain my identity in the face of increasing demands from family. And I wouldn't change a thing. In the next few years, I will probably see my youngest child go off to university and my life will change significantly again. Then, the weight of family and motherhood in my life's balance will decrease. And I will have other endeavours to pursue and challenges to face.

It is essential to create a system that works for your family life and to find what works for you to balance the areas of your life. I have developed a way to have it all—maybe not all at once, but in a way that beautifully balances for me. It is the balance of living well.

my family journal

Current Issue in Family (children, work, partner, health, etc.) _e.g., 12-year-old inconsistent in school_

performance

_____

_____

_____

_____

_____

_____

_____

Cause of Issue _e.g., poor study habits; excessive time spent on computer and TV_

_____

_____

_____

_____

_____

_____

_____

_____

_____

Workable Solution *e.g., decide together time limits on*

computer, TV etc.; review homework daily

_____

_____

_____

_____

_____

_____

_____

_____

_____

_____

_____

Record Results on a Weekly Basis
(may not apply to all issues)

1. *e.g., note-keeping has improved*

_____

_____

_____

_____

_____

2. _____

_____

_____

_____

_____

_____

3. _____

_____

_____

_____

_____

_____

4. _____

_____

_____

_____

_____

_____

_____

5. _____

_____

_____

_____

_____

friends
building
healthy
relationships

friends building
healthy relationships

Friends are an essential part of the wheel of life. My friends are always a part of my daily life. I eat, shop, and even exercise with my friends. They help keep my life in better balance. A good friendship is one of the best investments of your precious time. Friends provide companionship, inspiration, support, and laughter. As with all the other life elements, friendship is part of a healthy and balanced life.

My friendships with my two closest girlfriends are strong and essential building blocks in my life. This life segment is also the most flexible—it's truly yours to design. And it's often the answer to your needs. When I was raising four toddlers and feeling that I had no time for anything other than them, my friends helped keep me in touch with the world. I learned that if I wanted to maintain those special relationships, I too had to make an effort. I found that the only way to maintain my friendships was to work my friends into my new life, and only by combining all the elements of my life with my friends could I maintain balance and sanity.

For many of us, our days are jam-packed. Technology helps our day function more efficiently. This has both positives and negatives. With the internet, email, and BlackBerrys, having our agenda and the information we need at our fingertips should free up a lot of our time. But what's the number one complaint we all have? That there's not enough time in the day to do what we want to do. The simple reason is that since our lives are being made more efficient and we are getting so many more things done in our day, we are not using the free time to spend with our families, friends, or ourselves. We are simply taking on more work and making ourselves

"Friendship is one of the best investments of your precious time. Friends provide companionship, inspiration, support, and laughter."

busier. Doesn't quite make sense. And I am as guilty of it as anybody. But I realized that if I wanted to have a functioning family and a quality social life, while still addressing my needs, I had to plan my day better. Friends so often can be put on the back burner with the other demands of our lives, but I realized that that's a huge mistake.

How Friends Complete Us

I count myself as one of the lucky people where friends are concerned. My closest friends, whom I've known for most of my life, help fill in my life's gaps, to complete me, in so many ways. When you're spending morning until night taking care of your family's needs and endeavouring to meet work responsibilities and social obligations, a close friend often can be the only person around whom you can truly be yourself. I rely on my friends for so much: advice, support, commiseration, celebration, bouncing ideas off, bolstering sagging confidence, shoulders to cry on, and more. They have seen me through the many highs and lows of my days, with unconditional support. You can trust real friends because they don't compete with you. They

want the best for you, celebrate your successes, and help you through your struggles. And because they want the best for you, they bring out the best in you. So you can be confident that you are creating a truly supportive environment for one another no matter what you're discussing.

Friends also provide a support system in the absence of family. I see this with friends who live away from their families. They don't have the same support network that family usually provides when in the same city, so they rely on their friends to provide it. These same people talk about how difficult it can be to develop new friendships. But when they prioritize friendship, they often step outside their comfort zones and take the initiative in forging those friendships that they need. They make new friends through their children, their interests, their work, or by volunteering in their communities.

The same is true of anyone who feels they don't have enough of a friendship element in their lives, even if they do have the support network of family. They may have put so much time and energy into their careers, family, or into other areas of their lives that they neglected the friendship element. As they move into a new stage of life, they realize that they need to add friends in order to balance it. They decide to devote more time to meeting and making friends to give them a social outlet and to relax. They try new hobbies, sign up for classes, or join organizations—all of which creates opportunities for forming friendships. My husband and I have nurtured varied friendships, old and new, to enrich our lives. To me, each friend is like a different spice in my life—a different aroma, colour, and flavour.

Stop for a moment and ask yourself if you have given enough time and attention to your friends. If the answer is yes, consider yourself fortunate and your life richer for it. If the answer is no, this is an area to nurture.

Accepting the Good and the Bad

Wouldn't it be wonderful if everyone were perfect? Sometimes we can be the greatest critics of those around us. But we know we're not perfect, and nor are our friends. We need to weigh the good against the bad. If there are more good characteristics than bad ones, keep these friends. If you're too critical, you may end up living your life as a hermit. If a good friend has qualities that bother me, I try to avoid the situations or discussions where these traits surface. Or if we disagree on an issue—child rearing practices, for example—I try to avoid the topic when I'm with that friend. Another common disagreement is over the handling of money. Many of my friends don't see eye to eye with me when it comes to spending habits, so I avoid any discussion of this topic.

So, having reflected on the questions posed above, and taking into consideration that we all have our faults, you will have a pretty good idea who your most trustworthy and closest friends are. Even if you have only one friend, it's important to realize how fortunate you are that someone is there for you. If you feel you don't have any close friends, it's time to search, develop, and enrich some of your relationships.

Stop for a moment and ask yourself if you have given enough time and attention to your friends.
If the answer is yes, consider yourself fortunate and your life richer for it.

where am I now?

Do I have at least two friends whom I see or speak to at least twice a week? ☐ Yes ☐ No

If yes, do these friends know me, and do I know and understand them, on an emotional level?
☐ Yes ☐ No

Do I feel enthusiastic about seeing and speaking to them? ☐ Yes ☐ No

Do my friends make me feel good about myself?
☐ Yes ☐ No

Do my friends support me through my good and bad times? ☐ Yes ☐ No

Do my friends listen to my thoughts and ideas, and vice versa? ☐ Yes ☐ No

If you answered no to any of these questions, now's the time to re-evaluate your friendships. Chances are, these aren't the friends who will support you through your life, and they won't bring out the best in you. It is wise to spend some time developing better relationships.

Do my friends leave me feeling bored or even depressed? ☐ Yes ☐ No

Do they often leave me feeling angry, rejected, or criticized? ☐ Yes ☐ No

Do my friends often seem to think they are superior to me? ☐ Yes ☐ No

Do I feel as if I give more time and attention to my friends than vice versa? ☐ Yes ☐ No

Am I worried about being honest and confidential with my friends? ☐ Yes ☐ No

If you answered yes to any of these questions, you may want to re-evaluate your relationships. Again, these may not be the friends whom you are able to trust, who inspire you, or who support the person you are. However, having said that, it's important to realize that no one—and this includes your friends—is perfect.

where do I want to be?

Once you have a clearer understanding of which of your friendships are beneficial and supportive, it's time to ensure that these relationships are as good as they can be. These questions will help you work toward enriching the relationships that are worthwhile.

Can I make the effort to plan times to speak or visit with at least one of my best friends twice a week?　　　☐ Yes　　☐ No

If yes jot down when and where you can fit this into your busy schedule and what activity you might do together.

_____

_____

_____

_____

_____

_____

_____

If I have young children, are there toddler activities that a friend or acquaintance can join me in?　　　☐ Yes　　☐ No

If yes, what are at least two toddler activities in a week where I can have adult company?

1. _____

_____

2. _____

_____

If I find that I don't really have any close friends whom I can count on, do I have an acquaintance or colleague whom I might try to develop a better friendship with?　　　☐ Yes　　☐ No

Two people who share common interests with me and who may become closer friends are—

1. _____

2. _____

What can the first step in trying to establish a relationship be?

_____

_____

_____

_____

How was the most recent argument with a good friend resolved? What was the argument about and how did we both deal with it? Did I ignore it and move on or did I address the issues and clear the air?

_____

_____

_____

_____

If I wasn't happy with how the argument was handled, what might I have done differently?

_____

_____

_____

_____

When I'm excited about my life, do my friends want to hear all about it and do I feel they want to share in my joy? ☐ Yes ☐ No

How do my friends react when I talk about my accomplishments?

_____

_____

_____

_____

_____

_____

_____

When I have failures or feel depressed, do my friends give me the time I need?

☐ Yes ☐ No

How do my friends react to me when I'm feeling down?

_____

_____

_____

_____

_____

YOUR ANSWERS to the *where am I now* and the *where do I want to be* questions will give you a clear picture of the type of friends you have and whether you need to pay closer attention to those friendships. Or maybe you've come to the realization that the friendship is not one you wish to continue.

Let's now take a look at how to improve the friendships you do want to keep, so that you and your friends get the most out of them.

Wherever and Whatever It Takes

I've come to view time spent with my girlfriends as time that is essential to the balance of my life. Since my friends' lives are as busy as mine, we try to make the most of the time we do have with each other and to cherish it. And we are each committed to making time available for one another on a regular basis. Here are some of the ways I have incorporated friends into my life:

- When my children were young, I went to play-groups, museums, and zoos—places where I could be with my friends and my children at the same time.

- I invite my friends and their kids over for a coffee and snack, a simple brunch, or—especially when our spouses were working late or out of the house—for dinner. My friends who don't have the time to cook especially appreciate this. And I've discovered that more discussion happens over food than anywhere else. I love making my Grilled Chicken Caesar Salad with my friends in the kitchen (see page 167 for the recipe). We get to cook together, talk, and then share this healthy and delicious dish.

- I like to join a friend for window shopping, lunch, or even grocery shopping. There are lots of activities you can do in kid-friendly environments too.

- I attend an exercise class with a friend or invite her along on my early morning dog walk.

- My husband and I occasionally double date with one of my friends and her partner.

For the acquaintances whom I want to see but don't have time to on a regular basis, I get out my calendar and schedule a get-together with them a few times a year. Even if it's just a movie-and-coffee evening, it gives us a chance to catch up.

Of course, these strategies don't work with all the people in my life or at all times in my life. It can be a challenge getting together with those long-time friends whom I have less in common with today than I once did, those friends whom I've grown apart from over the years. But that's okay. Our needs evolve and change at different stages of our lives. And life's different stages can create opportunities, too. As my children are getting older and less dependent, I am finding more and more time for various friends. And I'm making an effort to make new friends, which is exciting and stimulating. Age is not a barrier: Some of my friends are older and some are younger.

Now that two of my four children are away at university, I have more time to spend with my husband as a couple or out with my friends. Let's not forget that your partner can often be your number one friend.

I read once that most people can count their close friends on one hand. I think this notion comes from an appreciation that for most people—and certainly this applies to me, with a husband, four children, four pets, a demanding career, and a schedule full with all the other elements of my life—there is limited time for friends. My Do One Thing Right rule reminds me to focus on the friendships that matter the most to me and to really invest in them, even if it means that I do not have the time to pursue friendships with some of the other amazing people I have met throughout my life.

Friends … Food … Fun

For some people, the thought of entertaining friends is stressful. They would prefer to go out to a movie together, to the gym, and so on. And that's the beauty of friends. Friends are so flexible that you can integrate them into other aspects of your life. In fact, friends can be the glue that holds your wheel of life together, in balance. Fitness with a friend, going shopping with a friend (the fashion segment of the wheel),

just spending time together is what's important.

One of the ways I try to make time spent with friends special is to make it fun, and it's no coincidence that when I think of fun, I usually think of food. It doesn't have to be a special occasion or an elaborate meal. Some of the best memories I have of laughter with good friends are of times gathered around a table just "breaking bread." Sometimes get-togethers with friends are at a favourite restaurant or a friend's cottage, but more often than not they're around my own kitchen or dining-room table. I combine my love of cooking with spending time with friends by asking them to drop in for a bite to eat—sometimes for a formal meal, sometimes for just a snack. The gift I can share with my friends is serving them delicious and nutritious foods. (Take a look at my favourite, and easy, recipes on page 163.) Even when I'm entertaining friends, I'm thinking of the balance in their lives.

Here are some tips to make entertaining friends easy:

1. **Invite people who have something in common with one another.** My husband and I have an eclectic mix of friends, whom we met through community work, business, the neighbourhood, and our children. I used to think that because they were friends of ours and we enjoyed them so much, all our guests would enjoy each other. I'd invite them to dinners and expect the conversation to flow.

Guess what? It didn't always work out so well. I've since learned my lesson. Now that I try to introduce people to those who share common interests or acquaintances, I've noticed that my dinner parties are more successful.

2. **Make the food preparation and serving appear effortless.** If you've been working for hours preparing the meal, don't admit it to your guests—it makes them feel less welcome. Pick a menu that is easy to manage. Your friends came to see you, and they won't enjoy themselves as much if you're slaving away in the kitchen much of the time they're there. Be organized and do as much food preparation in advance as possible. If you have to prepare something after your guests have arrived, enlist at least one of them to help you, so that both you and they are more relaxed. And don't try preparing a new menu that you've never tested. Experiments may not always work out as you hoped.

   If food preparation seems like too much to tackle, order take-out. Fresh, quality food doesn't have to be expensive. Or, if friends offer to bring a dish, take them up on their offer. The point is to spend time having fun together.

3. **Don't leave your guests unattended at the end of the evening to clean up.** Either leave the dishes until after your guests leave or allow one of them to help you. Of course, the more organized you are to start, the less work you'll have at the end of the evening.

4. **Dress comfortably.** Because you will be cooking and moving around a lot, pick clothing you can relax in. You don't want to feel like it's the end of the world if you splatter food on yourself. If you're comfortable, your friends will be comfortable too.

How to Nurture and Maintain Your Friendships

Friendships are relationships that need taking care of if you want them to grow and mature. I have learned over the years how to maintain successful, productive, long-lasting, and supportive friendships. These friendships can be exciting, intimate, stimulating, and intense. Here are a few rules I abide by to keep my relationships going strong:

• Give your friends the privacy and space they need when they don't want to divulge all their thoughts and emotions. When they're ready, when they feel you will accept them unconditionally, they'll let you in on their lives. This takes time.

• Be a good listener and encourage your friends to talk about themselves. While criticizing and condemning will make your friends withdraw, constructive criticism at the right time is beneficial.

- Every so often let your friends know how precious your relationship with them is to you. This makes your friends feel important and enriches the relationships.

- Accept and respect each other's differences and opinions. Try to see your friends' points of view and vow to never say, "You're wrong." Remind yourself why you're friends.

- The best way to deal with an argument is to avoid it in the first place. Knowing your friends' triggers is key.

- During a disagreement, someone has to let go of his or her ego. Even if you feel your friend is in the wrong, step forward and in some fashion say you're sorry. Once some time has passed, you may want to revisit the discussion and calmly restate your view—doing so may get rid of buried bad feelings, clearing the air.

- If similar disagreements keep creeping up, it's time for a face-to-face discussion, with the rule that neither of you raises your voice or walks away.

- Always be a good friend to those closest to you. This is not an easy task. You need to be honest, loyal, dependable, open, responsive, supportive, sincere, and, most importantly, always there.

- Try not to be too busy to see your closest friends. This may be the greatest challenge of all when it comes to friendships. If you haven't heard from your friend in a while, take the initiative and call, even if you're busy.

- Every so often review your relationships to make sure that your friends are a positive influence in your life.

Take a look at the chart on friendships at the end of the chapter (see page 110). Fill it out, then look carefully at what you've written. It may give you the clearest picture yet of those friends you truly want next to you and those who may not be as good for you.

There are plenty of reasons we lose contact with friends. Whatever the reasons, they're probably not good ones. In this era of email, affordable long-distance telephone rates, and inexpensive airfares, it's easy to keep in touch. Good friends are a valuable commodity. I have always worked hard to maintain my closest friendships, even through the busiest periods of my life. Friends provide perspective. They help you to see the forest as well as the trees. Making the time for friends who represent your family of need and of choice is the perfect way to complete the balance of your life.

determining my true friends

Under each heading, write an example that illustrates that point. Your answers will allow you to clearly see who your true friends are.

Names of Closest Friends

_____

_____

_____

_____

_____

_____

_____

_____

Names of Close Acquaintances

_____

_____

_____

_____

_____

_____

_____

_____

Listens to you and offers solid advice

_____

_____

_____

_____

_____

Accepts who you are

_____

_____

_____

_____

Enjoys your success

_____

_____

_____

_____

Lets you know you are a good friend

_____

_____

_____

_____

Types of arguments and how they're solved

_____

_____

_____

_____

_____

_____

_____

_____

_____

_____

_____

_____

_____

_____

_____

_____

_____

_____

fashion
looking
my best

fashion looking my best

What is fashion? It's style, beauty, clothing, shoes, makeup. It's attitude. It's a means of expressing ourselves, and it often represents how we are feeling inside. It's a visual tool we use to communicate a certain image to others. Fashion definitely plays a role in the first impression we make. It may not be of number one priority in your wheel of life, but how you present yourself is important nonetheless.

When I have confidence in how I look, this transfers over to my family and friends. Your finances may dictate somewhat how you dress, but it is not a barrier to looking great. You may just have to be a smarter shopper.

Whatever the occasion—whether it's a job interview or simply a stroll down the street—feeling that you look up-to-date and attractive boosts your confidence. And more confidence is never a bad thing: There's no question that you're at your best when you're confident.

Until recently, fashion wasn't much of a priority for me. Not because I don't like clothes and shoes and perfume and jewellery. I love all those things, but I felt I really hadn't the time to worry

too much about how I looked from head to toe—my focus was more on staying in good physical shape. Of course, I have always tried to keep somewhat fashionable. But I just didn't devote a lot of effort to being totally coordinated; style always seemed to be hit and miss with me. If I got the slacks and top right, the shoes were wrong. If the shoes and belt were great, they didn't match the outfit. And colour coordination? That always confused me. Being truly fashionable seemed like hard and time-consuming work. Shopping and constantly having my hair done in the salon, keeping up on the latest trends, primping and preening took too much time—time I didn't have to spare (never mind

"Whatever the occasion—whether it's a job interview or simply a stroll down the street—feeling that you look up-to-date and attractive boosts your confidence."

that I figured it would cost a fortune). I was busy getting a business going, writing cookbooks, raising four children, car-pooling, making meals for my family, helping with homework, walking the dogs, and working on maintaining a healthy marriage and friendships. Yes, I wanted to look nice, but a lot of other things came first.

As my schedule began to fill up with speaking engagements and television appearances, I realized that fashion might have to be more of a priority for me. Coco Chanel was once quoted as saying, "Dress shabbily, they notice the dress; dress impeccably, they notice the woman!" Chanel wasn't very often wrong about how to dress. Maybe this was something I was going to have to investigate in more detail.

At about the same time, I recalled an article I had read several years earlier that discussed what the various New York fashion editors would be wearing that particular year. Anna Wintour, the famous editor of *Vogue* magazine, had apparently adopted the "new minimalism" philosophy: She would have only nine or so items of clothing in her closet for the fall/winter season. Everything would be either black or white, and everything would match. The two suits each had a skirt and

slacks. The two blouses could be worn with either suit. The jackets could be switched between the suits or worn with her wardrobe's one dress. To go with these nine items, she would have a great black coat and gloves, one black handbag that would match with everything, three pairs of black shoes, and a pair of black boots. She told the interviewer that paring down your wardrobe to a very few high-quality, workable, essential pieces was both stylish and time-saving. French women have been doing this for years. It sounded simple, effective, and doable.

With such a minimalist philosophy, I could cut down the time I spent making a decision about which outfit to wear to a few seconds. It was a simple and easy system for looking fashionable at work. And I didn't have to buy cost-a-fortune couture to look stylish. There were plenty of affordable designers who made classic clothes that would be great for me. Even if I spent more money than I might usually on a single piece or on each piece of clothing I did buy, with so few items of clothing in my closet, I would save money in the long run.

But a bunch of black-and-white business clothing wasn't going to take me out dog-walking, shopping, or to a friend's dinner party. If this system was to work for me, I would need to restrict this new minimalism to my work clothes. I would develop what amounted to a consistent "uniform" for work, but I would stick with what I had for casual clothing, with maybe a few additions to update those outfits.

But where to start? What had seemed simple and efficient was suddenly looking like a big and complicated job. When in doubt, I bring to mind my mantra, Do One Thing Right. And so that's what I did.

Creating My New Look

Before heading to the store, I needed to make some room in my closet. Even though I regularly purge my kids' wardrobes of clothing that is worn out or no longer fits, and I thought I had been doing the same for mine, my closet was jam-packed. On close inspection, I saw that there definitely was clothing that wouldn't fit with my new minimalist philosophy. I realized that the purges of my closet had been restricted to my most casual clothing. I hadn't minded getting rid of tired-looking khakis, track pants, or faded sweatshirts, but over the years I had kept every suit or party outfit I had paid a decent amount of money for. I could see that many of them were really out of date, but if something was well made and of good-quality fabric, I had kept it, thinking it might come back into style or that I could alter it to look more fashionable.

This was when I knew I had to bring in an objective third party, a friend whom I trusted to be completely honest with me and whose taste I felt was above reproach. But before we even looked in my closet, I was surprised to learn that she thought there was a more urgent matter than my wardrobe overhaul to attend to.

The Makeover

My girlfriend told me that my haircut and colour was really in need of an update. I had been wearing my hair and makeup exactly the same way for the last 20 years. She said that she thought I could look fresher and younger with a slightly shorter and sportier cut and a more flattering colour. I have to admit that I resisted changing my hair. The style I had could be washed and blown dry fast—put on a little bit of makeup and I could be out the door in about 20 minutes.

Finally I let her persuade me, and off we went to the beauty salon. My hairstylist, whom I had been going to for years, was thrilled when she learned I was thinking about a change. She suggested a shorter, layered style and a lighter, richer shade of brown. My friend agreed, and I, reluctantly and somewhat skeptically, took the plunge. But I needn't have worried. I loved the result. My look is now younger and more polished. Styling my new haircut at home took a little getting used to, but once I mastered it, it was just as easy as my old hairstyle had been. But best of all were the compliments I received about looking younger and more in style.

Next we went shopping for makeup to augment the products I already had. With my new hair colour, slightly deeper shades of blush and lipstick looked better. And natural taupe and plum eyeshadows also looked great—they weren't extreme, but made me look younger and more vibrant. The cosmetician taught me to apply the makeup so that it looked natural.

The Purge

Now we were ready to tackle that closet of mine. The first thing my girlfriend told me was that I needed to put aside my pack-rat tendencies. Her rule of thumb is that if you haven't worn something in two years, it's time to get rid of it. This was by far the hardest thing to do when it came to organizing my clothes. Following her rule sure eliminated a lot of things, and at first it made me nervous. After a while, though, I found that I actually felt a little thrill of exhilaration as I took control of my closet.

After those clothes had been put in boxes for donation, I tried on all the casual clothes, business outfits, party clothes, and shoes that were left, while my friend gave me her candid opinion on each. Once I relaxed, we had fun— and some good laughs over items I had once worn. How I had loved those padded shoulders and jumpsuits!

After the purge was complete, what I was left with for work clothes were a few good basics. There was a black skirt and a couple of pairs of black slacks that fit me well. I had a black sweater with a flattering neckline and two pairs of boots that we agreed looked right. On the casual clothing front, I had many more winners. All in all, it was exciting to have a fresh start with my clothes. Everything that we had decided to keep fit me well and was in style. I could now easily make up my list of what I needed to fill in the gaps. I knew that I didn't have to buy it all at once. I could budget for the priority items and buy the rest on sale as I found them.

The New You

So, are your hair, makeup, or clothes in need of makeovers, like mine were? The dead giveaway that I should think about making a change was that I answered yes to the question, Am I still wearing the same hair and makeup I was 20 years ago? How about you? Even 5 or 10 years is probably too long. To evaluate your hair and makeup, ask yourself the following questions. If you are unsure of the answers, check with a friend whose taste you admire. Your hairstylist can also be helpful.

hair
where am I now?

Does my haircut suit the shape of my face?

☐ Yes ☐ No

Is my hair colour flattering to my skin tone?

☐ Yes ☐ No

Is my hair cut and colour age appropriate?

☐ Yes ☐ No

Does my hairstyle suit my job and my lifestyle?

☐ Yes ☐ No

Is my hair healthy—shiny and bouncy?

☐ Yes ☐ No

Can I do my hair in a relatively short time?

☐ Yes ☐ No

If you have answered no to some of these questions, a trip to the salon might be in order. It's always a good idea to have a consultation with your hairstylist before doing anything drastic. Many of us look at magazine models' hair for inspiration. But often these styles, although they look great, are high maintenance, requiring either lots of styling time or constant trims to keep them looking top-notch. You might also consider volunteering to be featured in one of the makeovers offered by a local television show or magazine.

where do I want to be?

Can I easily do my hair each day so it has the look I'm after? ☐ Yes ☐ No

Is my hairstyle affordable to keep it looking its best? ☐ Yes ☐ No

Can I do different things with my hairstyle so I can have a variety of looks? ☐ Yes ☐ No

Once you decide you want to make a hairstyle change, it's time to seek a bit of advice (if you have a teenaged daughter as I do, likely you are getting lots of advice already):

● Ask your friends for their opinions.

● Consult a trusted hairstylist.

● Flip through the hairstyle magazines at your salon.

Once you've selected a style, make sure your hairstylist agrees that your hair type can perform in the style you want. For example, a woman with thin and straight, wispy hair will not be able to get her hair to look full and wavy easily. And if you have thick, curly hair, you will have to spend a fair bit of time with a round brush and blow dryer if you want a straight style. It's easier and quicker in the long run if you select a style your hair will naturally adapt to. Ask your hairstylist to teach you how to style your new look at home.

If you plan to change or add colour, make sure you understand what will be involved in maintaining it. If colouring means frequent trips to the salon that you don't have time for or can't afford, rethink your options. Maybe you can manage the colour with an at-home product, or maybe there's a lower maintenance alternative. Other things to consider before colouring your hair are whether you'll need to use a gentler shampoo designed specially for colour-treated hair and whether you'll need to keep your hair out of the sun to prevent the colour from changing or fading quickly.

makeup
where am I now?

Is my skin tone uneven, and would foundation makeup improve its look?   ☐ Yes   ☐ No

If I wear foundation, does it match my skin tone?   ☐ Yes   ☐ No

Does the foundation contain SPF 15 or higher sunblock?   ☐ Yes   ☐ No

Do I have natural-looking colours of blush and lipstick that suit me?   ☐ Yes   ☐ No

Do I have flattering shades of eyeshadow and eyeliner, and do I know how to apply them?   ☐ Yes   ☐ No

Are my eyebrows nicely shaped—natural-looking and not overplucked?   ☐ Yes   ☐ No

The questions above will point you toward what you need for a simple yet functional makeup kit. For me, simple and speedy are the keys to being polished each morning when I go out the door. Once I've applied my makeup at home, all I need to put in my handbag is a powder compact, blush, and a lipstick, and I'm ready for the day.

where do I want to be?

Does my makeup suit the environment I'm in?

☐ Yes ☐ No

Does my makeup take a minimal amount of time to apply?

☐ Yes ☐ No

Does my makeup still look fresh a few hours after I apply it?

☐ Yes ☐ No

Is my makeup age appropriate? ☐ Yes ☐ No

When it comes to makeup, I believe that in most cases, less is more. But it also helps to have the right makeup and to apply it correctly. As with hair, there are lots of resources available to help you make a change. Here are a few makeup tips I've learned along the way:

1. When selecting makeup colours, pick shades that naturally enhance your skin, hair, and eye colour. In makeup, subtle is definitely better. For evening, simply apply these same colours but in slightly more depth.

2. Visit a department store or drugstore that carries a good makeup selection and spend some time with the cosmetics consultant. These consultants are usually very knowledgeable and can show you how to apply your makeup correctly and in a flattering way. Be aware though that the cosmeticians are there to sell you product, so have a clear idea of what you need before you shop. You may wish to bring your existing makeup bag with you to the store—you will be less tempted to buy new products when you can see what you already have.

3. With foundation or powder, spending a bit more money for a good-quality product is well worth it. Cheaper foundations and powders can look cakey or chalky, which is certainly not natural-looking and can make you look older than your years.

The American journalist Diane Sawyer was once asked which brand of mascara she used. She replied that she liked the cheap drugstore kind because the expensive mascaras she'd tried weren't dark enough and flaked onto her skin after only about an hour of wear. I agree with her. I have bought expensive mascara only once and it didn't perform well for me. I favour the newest and best-priced mascara my local drugstore has to offer. But, of course, it is a personal choice.

The makeup resource book I highly recommend is Paula Begoun's *Don't Go to the Cosmetics Counter Without Me!* You can't beat this book for debunking the claims that many $200 cosmetic products make. Paula can point to a $15 product that will work just as well or even better.

About the eyebrows—I've learned that having naturally shaped eyebrows can make all the difference to the appearance of your eyes, and they can create a frame for your entire face. And speaking of tweezers, here's a tip I want to pass along: Keep a pair of tweezers in the car and in your handbag. That way, if you spot a stray chin hair—you know those hairs that women of a "certain age" get—in the washroom at the office or in the rear-view mirror (daylight is great light for catching these kinds of things. Remember though, only at the red light!) you're not stuck with it for the rest of the day. There is a pink Swiss Army knife designed especially for women that has a great set of tweezers.

Cleansing

It's a good idea to periodically re-evaluate your facial cleansing regime. It doesn't have to include expensive products to work well. But your skin's needs change substantially over time. As we age, our skin often needs a gentler cleanser and a richer moisturizer than it once did. Drinking eight cups of water a day can do more for you than anything else to keep your skin hydrated. And don't forget about the sunblock and makeup with sunscreen added. Sun damage can be serious. Here are a few more things to keep in mind:

1. When it comes to maintaining your skin, trial and error is often the only way to find what works for you. Ask your friends what products and brands they like.

2. Know your skin type and use products that address your particular issues.

3. Don't forget to exfoliate—gentle exfoliation forces skin to rejuvenate itself, which helps maintain a youthful glow.

4. Again, the cosmetics consultants at the department stores and drugstores are usually very helpful. But be aware that it is the cosmetic companies that employ the consultants at their department store counters, meaning these consultants will sell you only their companies' products. Drugstore cosmeticians work for the store rather than any one cosmetic company, so they tend to

be less biased in favour of a specific brand. However, they are rewarded for selling you high-cost items. Aestheticians who perform facials in salons also know a lot about skin care, but they tend to promote the products their salon carries.

5. A visit to a dermatologist can be helpful if you have any serious concerns about your skin. These professionals not only treat skin conditions but are on the leading edge when it comes to anti-aging. However, anti-aging treatments are not covered by most public health plans, and they can be very expensive. Start taking care of your skin at an early age and the results will pay off in years to come.

Nails

And last but definitely not least on the grooming front is your nails. There has been a boom in the manicure and pedicure business in the last several years. That's because it has become a fashion crime to wear open-toed shoes or sandals without pedicured toenails. Although the hottest new colour is constantly changing, natural is always in. A sheer polish in a pale ivory or ballet pink is all you need for both toenails and fingernails. When that nail polish on your fingers starts to chip, either touch it up or remove it. Often I don't have the time to keep up manicures, so I simply keep a clear polish on my nails. It keeps me looking well groomed. With nail salons popping up everywhere, offering fast and inexpensive manicures and pedicures, why not treat yourself to a visit once in a while? It's important to pick a salon that has stringent cleanliness policies. Salons and spas in North America are not under government regulation, even though a number of serious health risks are associated with various procedures performed by aestheticians:

1. Hepatitis B and C, plantar warts, herpetic whitlow (an inflammation near the nails), and even HIV can be transmitted when salons do not adequately sterilize manicure tools. There have been numerous documented incidents in North America of serious viral illnesses being transmitted in this way.

2. All kinds of mycobacterial skin conditions and rashes can develop when basins or whirlpools, especially throne-style whirlpool chairs that recirculate water, are not properly sterilized between uses. They can be bacterial breeding grounds. Staphylococcus, streptococcus, and nail fungus are risks if proper sterilization procedures are not followed.

3. Foot buffers also need to be properly cleaned or they may transfer infection.

4. Be observant and don't be afraid to ask questions. Once you've found a salon or spa you trust, have fun and relax. Treat yourself to a spa day with a girlfriend.

wardrobe
where am I now?

You've analyzed your hairstyle, makeup, and grooming system. Now it's time to take a close look at your clothes. How you look and what you wear is often a reflection of how you feel about yourself.

Do my clothes fit me well? ☐ Yes ☐ No

Does my wardrobe make me look stylish and pulled together? ☐ Yes ☐ No

Am I dressing in an age-appropriate way? ☐ Yes ☐ No

Am I dressing appropriately for the job I have? ☐ Yes ☐ No

When I get dressed in the morning, is it fast and easy to put together an outfit? ☐ Yes ☐ No

Do I spend what I can realistically afford on clothes? ☐ Yes ☐ No

Am I dressing in a flattering manner for my body shape? ☐ Yes ☐ No

Am I wearing colours that suit me? ☐ Yes ☐ No

Have I tried wearing various colours, patterns, and textures? ☐ Yes ☐ No

Do I have accessories that accent and add personality to my clothing? ☐ Yes ☐ No

If I'm at home taking care of children or if I work at home, do I still take care of my appearance? ☐ Yes ☐ No

Have I kept my femininity and sexuality instead of blending into a domestic blur? ☐ Yes ☐ No

If most of your answers were yes, I bet you look great when you leave the house, and even when you stay at home. If some of your answers were no, keep reading. You'll need to figure out a flattering and attractive look for yourself.

where do I want to be?

What is the kind of look I like and would feel comfortable in?

_____
_____
_____
_____
_____
_____
_____
_____
_____
_____
_____
_____
_____
_____
_____
_____

Will this look suit my body type or can it be adapted to suit me? ☐ Yes ☐ No

Is it appropriate for the work and activities I engage in during the day? ☐ Yes ☐ No

How much money can I spend on fashion in a year, including beauty items? $ _____

Take some time to figure out what style and colours you like and make note of what others wear that looks especially flattering. To be minimalist in your approach, make sure the look is adaptable to the various situations you regularly encounter.

First things first, though, and that means purging your existing wardrobe. Sort through your clothes and get rid of any that fall into one or more of these categories:

- doesn't fit well and most likely never will

- worn out

- in poor taste

- out of date (and can't be salvaged with new accessories or shoes)

- haven't worn in two years

If you are like me, not confident about deciding all this by yourself, bring in someone you trust to help you. Having a friend help can dramatically cut down the time it takes to make the decisions, and it can make the process fun as well. If you are nervous about getting rid of clothes you think of as being borderline, or the two-year rule is just out of the question, store the items in question in your basement or in a separate box for a year or so—making sure, of course, that they are kept dry and out of harm's (and bugs') way. Then congratulate yourself on a job well done.

The next step is to reassemble your wardrobe with select items. Many clothing stores have personal shoppers who will work with you on building your wardrobe. They're also happy to work within your budget. High-end stores often supply this service, usually free of charge.

Whether you seek the help of a personal shopper or choose to put together your new wardrobe on your own, the list of clothing items opposite will help you put your look together. Together these pieces represent a complete wardrobe for each season. Choose the ones appropriate for your lifestyle. Although planning your wardrobe for the entire year might seem overwhelming at first, by doing so you will end up saving money—because you won't buy ill-thought-out items on a whim—and time shopping. Many of these items you may already have in your newly purged wardrobe.

Review the clothing list with a couple of questions in mind. First, what items of clothing do you need? Don't forget to include shoes, boots, jewellery, and handbags. Black or brown shoes and handbags will go with just about everything, potentially saving you lots of money. Don't forget about any undergarments you might also need. You don't want a white bra showing through a black blouse or panty lines under your slacks. Second, for what occasions and activities do you need a specific style or

Your Clothing List

Fall/Winter

2 suits, each with jacket, slacks, and matching skirt ☐

1 jacket or blazer ☐

2 pairs slacks (other than the suit slacks) ☐

2 dresses ☐

2 slim-fitting sweaters for beneath jackets ☐

2 blouses ☐

1 coat ☐

2 pairs shoes ☐

1 pair boots ☐

Casual and Workout

2 pairs jeans or casual pants ☐

2 to 3 fitted shirts ☐

2 sweatsuits and/or shorts and T-shirt ☐

2 pairs sports shoes (1 for athletics, 1 for casual sports dress) ☐

Accessories

jewellery, including costume ☐

handbag ☐

gloves ☐

shawl or scarf ☐

3 belts, each a different colour and style ☐

Spring/Summer

2 dresses ☐

2 pairs cropped or capri trousers ☐

2 pairs slacks ☐

1 jacket or blazer ☐

T-shirts—well fitted, different colours ☐

2 pairs shoes—1 flat, 1 heels ☐

Casual and Workout

2 pairs shorts ☐

T-shirts ☐

2 bathing suits and cover-up ☐

1 pair flip-flops or casual sandals ☐

Accessories

jewellery, including costume ☐

handbag ☐

Item	Season	Approximate Cost
1. dress shoes	fall	$125
2.		
3.		
4.		
5.		
6.		
7.		
8.		
9.		
10.		
11.		
12.		
13.		
14.		
		TOTAL

type of clothing? Do you have romp-around clothes for your mom-and-tot group; or an evening dress or a mix-and-match suit with pants, skirt, and shirt for the theatre you buy seasons' subscriptions to; or fashionable jeans and T-shirts or fitness outfits for strolling in?

Next, using the table above, prioritize each item in order of importance and assign each a cost estimate. You don't want to ruin all the good work you will do in the next chapter, on finance, in one fell swoop in this section!

How does the total of your cost estimates compare to the amount you noted previously that you could spend in a year? If it's substantially higher, consider spreading the purchases over more than one year.

Do you have extra items on your To Buy list that aren't accounted for above? Write them down here as a reminder—but remember, this is a minimalist system.

Item _____   Approximate Cost _____

Item _____   Approximate Cost _____

Item _____   Approximate Cost _____

If all this looks overwhelming—and it might, if you're starting from near scratch—remember, even if all you buy this fall is one great winter coat and a pair of boots, you'll have upped your fashion factor significantly. If changing your style is a priority but you have a very tight budget, don't forget about discount shopping. I love discount and clearance outlet malls—you can find fabulous designer items at drastically reduced prices. How do you think many fashion-conscious women look so good? End-of-season sales are another great place to find bargains on otherwise too-expensive items.

If you stick to classic designs, you'll only need to do a major wardrobe overhaul once, adding fresh pieces every few years. I find that often all it takes to update many items of clothing is a great pair of shoes, a piece of jewellery, a belt, or a scarf. A trip to the seamstress for an alteration is another easy way to refresh a tired outfit.

Keep in mind, though, that what looked great on you in your thirties won't necessarily look as good when you're in your forties or fifties, so you will want to periodically review your wardrobe and makeup and hair to see if it needs tweaking. The thing I like about this system is that it took the mystery out of fashion for me. It was never my ambition to be a cutting-edge fashionista. I just wanted to look modern, appropriate, and stylish on a budget.

I can tell you from experience, once you feel you've got a versatile "uniform" put together, it takes a lot of the uncertainty and extra time out of getting ready for any occasion. My husband thinks I look great in my new streamlined wardrobe and spunky haircut. (He also appreciates how fast I can get ready, too.) And I have to admit, I love the compliments I've received. Often people can't pinpoint the specifics; they'll just say, "You look terrific" or "Have you been on holiday?" or "What's different? You look really well." The best comment is, "You look younger." I now enjoy dressing more, wherever I go—even if only to the movies or grocery shopping. I like feeling put together. It builds my confidence knowing that I am prepared to be well dressed in minutes no matter what my day or night throws at me. Even jeans and a sweater look better on me, now that I've thought out the colours and fit.

Maintaining Your Wardrobe

So now that you have your wardrobe all figured out, you need to keep it looking fresh and as new as the day you bought it. Whether you take items to the dry cleaner or wash them yourself makes no difference. But nothing looks worse than scuffed shoes, a stained shirt, or unpressed pants—even your number one designer dress will look terrible if it's creased. Maintaining your wardrobe may be a bit time-consuming, but it's time you must find if you want to look well groomed. Set up a procedure to keep everything groomed. On Saturday morning I take a quick overview of my shoes, bags, and clothing. I put aside those items that need a "fix me up" and take care of it over the weekend so that, at the beginning of the week, I'm fresh to go.

Mind, Body, and Spirit

Whether we like it or not, people's first impressions are very tied up with how we look. As I said earlier, I am passionate about communicating my message of healthy, balanced living to people. I've noticed that when I look great, my message seems to have greater credibility: My appearance really does affect the way in which people listen and respond to me. Helping people achieve balance is my life's work, and succeeding in that work positively affects my mind and elevates my spirit. Feeling more confident about how I look takes the stress out of personal and television appearances, leaving me able to focus on the content of my message. Feeling confident in everyday life is a gift I feel I've earned by taking care of myself. And less stress definitely is good for my body at any time.

I look at fashion as a tool I use for my work. And now that it's easy for me to understand, it's also just plain fun. I don't rank the fashion building block as high in my life as those of family, food, fitness, and finance, but it is still important to the balance of my life; it's something I do just for me. I like to dress as if today is as important as any other—even if I'm slouching around the house or running errands. It makes me feel confident about myself and how I appear to others. Even the store clerk reacts to me differently when I'm put together. This doesn't mean I'm dressed formally or uncomfortably; it just looks like my appearance matters to me. Achieving a look and style that works is a dynamic process, one that is constantly changing. It's up to us to keep abreast of these changes. I posed a lot of specific questions in this chapter for you to reflect on. The fashion journal at the end of this chapter, on page 132, is a basic worksheet that will help keep you on track as your look and style evolves.

You can find fabulous designer items at drastically reduced prices at discount and outlet malls. How do you think many fashion-conscious women look so good?

my
fashion journal

Current State of Fashion	What Do I Want to Change and Why?
HAIR e.g., same for 10 years	*I look older than my years. Need fresh look.*
CLOTHING Work Casual Evening	
MAKEUP Daytime Evening	
TOTAL OVERALL LOOK Daytime Evening	

Practical Possible Solutions	Action Taken
Cover grey, add highlights.	Layered cut with auburn highlights, grey covered.

finance
managing my money

finance managing my money

Just bringing up the subject of money makes some people nervous. How much money we have—or don't have—is a personal, private matter, one that in most cultures is considered rude to discuss. Yet it's often one of the most important and contentious areas of our lives. What you spend your money on, how it's managed, how you deal with your debt, your credit rating, and how you increase your savings and investments all have to be managed if your financial situation is to be balanced. Your financial life can represent joy and freedom in your life, or it can make you feel like a victim. Choose the first. Finance tends to be a primary focus in one's wheel of life.

People often let money dictate who their friends are, how they eat, the type of fitness they pursue, how they dress, and how their family operates day to day. While finance obviously plays a part in the other segments of your life, you must not allow it to dictate how you live. You always have choices.

I believe that achieving financial success does not necessarily equate to being happy, and vice versa. It's what you do with the money that you do have that brings emotional well-being. Being on top of your personal finance means having an understanding of your savings, spending, taxes, insurance, investing, and planning.

For there to be balance, you must connect your financial goals and issues to the other areas of your life. For example, if your income allows you to have all the material objects

> "Our financial health and well-being has a direct and dramatic impact on each of the other elements of our lives."

you've ever desired, but your long hours at work don't allow you to spend time with your family, your life is unbalanced. Or, if you follow your passion in terms of career but this means you can't afford your monthly rent, your life will again be out of balance.

Our financial health and well-being has a direct and dramatic impact on each of the other elements of our lives. Having the financial means to provide for your children's education, family vacations, home improvements, your retirement needs, and those little extras helps take the stress out of everyday family life. Being able to afford sports equipment and various lessons helps keep your whole family fit. Fresh food may cost more than junk food, but we all want to be able to afford to make food that's good for us a priority. It goes without saying that it costs a bit of money to look fashionable. And, while you can enjoy a friend's company without spending money, it sure is nice to be able to afford the occasional dinner and a movie or to entertain once in a while.

It's Never Too Late

Despite the robust growth we've seen in the economy over the last few years, many advisors feel we are headed for trouble. On a personal level, we are at record-high levels of debt, with record-low levels of savings. Recent polls show that the majority of us are not financially prepared for retirement. The common problems seem to be—

- not planning, and procrastinating about our financial future
- overspending and saving too little
- increased credit card debt
- ineffective saving for retirement
- inadequate investments
- insufficient insurance
- emotional decisions affecting our financial thinking

The good news is that improving your finances is not rocket science—it simply requires tradeoffs and discipline. Financial advisors tell us it's never too late to put our finances in order. Most likely you'll have to examine your spending habits and slowly take steps to reduce your spending. Remember, as with implementing every other life change, small steps will get you to where you want to be.

If your debt situation has gotten away from you, you may need professional assistance right away. Most communities have not-for-profit credit counselling services; look in the Yellow Pages. A lawyer can also point you in the right direction. Consulting with an accredited accountant is another good place to start. Being prepared as you go into your first meeting with a professional will allow you to provide them with a clear picture of your finances.

The good news is that improving your finances is not rocket science—it simply requires trade-offs and discipline.

where am I now?

Is my income consistent with my lifestyle and with the future? ☐ Yes ☐ No

Am I in debt? ☐ Yes ☐ No

If yes, what is the debt?

_____

_____

_____

_____

_____

_____

_____

_____

_____

_____

_____

_____

_____

_____

Do I save a certain percentage of my monthly income? ☐ Yes ☐ No

How much? $ _____

Does this give me the security I need?

☐ Yes ☐ No

What security level do I want? $_____

Is my discretionary spending in line with my income and lifestyle? ☐ Yes ☐ No

Have my investments paid off? ☐ Yes ☐ No

Itemize investments

1. _____

_____

_____

_____

_____

2. _____

_____

_____

_____

3. _____

_____

_____

_____

Have I planned financially for my retirement?

☐ Yes ☐ No

If yes, what are these plans?

_____

_____

_____

_____

_____

_____

_____

_____

_____

_____

_____

_____

_____

_____

_____

_____

_____

where do I want to be?

Are my debts manageable?   ☐ Yes   ☐ No

If no, how serious is the situation?

_____

_____

_____

Do I have discretionary income for holidays, children's requests, and other non-essential items?   ☐ Yes   ☐ No

Do I have enough in savings for unforeseen circumstances?   ☐ Yes   ☐ No

If not, how will I manage the situation?

_____

_____

_____

Do I have a plan of how I'll lead my life when I reach retirement?   ☐ Yes   ☐ No

Am I happy with my financial picture?
   ☐ Yes   ☐ No

If no, what is my plan?

_____

_____

_____

_____

_____

_____

At what age do I expect to retire?

Age: _____

Number of years from now: _____

How much money in cash and assets will I need to retire at that age? (Consult with a professional if necessary.) $ _____

Is this a realistic goal? ☐ Yes   ☐ No

If no, what are my plans?

_____

_____

_____

_____

_____

_____

_____

_____

_____

_____

_____

_____

_____

_____

Where do I plan to live?

_____

_____

_____

_____

_____

_____

Will I want to budget for travel? ☐ Yes   ☐ No

If yes, how much? $ _____

What big items do I want to purchase before retirement?

Item	Year of Planned Purchase	Estimated Cost
_____	_____	_____
_____	_____	_____
_____	_____	_____
_____	_____	_____
_____	_____	_____
_____	_____	_____
_____	_____	_____
_____	_____	_____

Your Financial Picture

Your answers to the questions on the previous page likely give you a general idea of what condition your finances are in. But to fully understand your current financial state, you need to determine your assets and liabilities. Let's start with your assets.

Assets

Assets are the things that have value.

How much cash is in your bank accounts (both savings and chequing)?   +$ _____

Do you have any cheques written against that amount or any automatic monthly debits that will be withdrawn? If so, how much will be deducted from the cash balance this month?

–$ _____

Do you own all or part of a major asset: house; recreational property (cottage, ski chalet); vehicle (car, motorcycle, boat); stocks, bonds, or GICs? (TVs and computers don't count because they lose their value too quickly. Jewellery, furs, and art can be deceptive as to their market value, which is often much less than was paid for them.)   ☐ Yes   ☐ No

List these assets:

_____

_____

_____

_____

How much of these assets do you own outright (have equity in)? Write down the approximate amount for each. (You might need to call your banker or lender to determine the answer.)

EQUITY

House _____

Recreational property _____

Car _____

Motorcycle _____

Boat _____

Financial instruments: stocks, bonds, GICs

_____

Other (_____) _____

Other (_____) _____

Other (_____) _____

Other (_____) _____

TOTAL   **+$** _____

Liabilities

Now it's time to look at your liabilities. These are your debts. There's no doubt that thinking about what you owe can be overwhelming. But it's an important step in learning where you are financially. Once you understand your financial situation, you'll be able, over time, to solve any of your financial issues. So, keep focused on doing One Thing Right. Remember, too, that while there is bad debt, such as balances owing on credit cards, there is also good debt, involving, for instance, investing in the future.

Let's start with what you owe on the assets—your mortgage, car loan, and so on. Also, record the interest rate you are paying for each.

DEBT	INTEREST RATE (%)
House _____	_____
Recreational property _____	_____
Car _____	_____
Motorcycle _____	_____
Boat _____	_____

Financial instruments: stocks, bonds, GICs

_____

Other (_____)	_____
Other (_____)	_____
Other (_____)	_____
Other (_____)	_____
TOTAL	–$ _____

Now you need to calculate any other debt you have. What are your other liabilities? How much do you owe on credit cards? List the value of any liabilities you have that aren't listed above, along with the rates of interest you are paying on these debts.

DEBT	INTEREST RATE (%)
Visa	_____
MasterCard	_____
American Express	_____
Department store cards	_____
Gas cards	_____
Other (_____)	_____
Other (_____)	_____
Other (_____)	_____
Other (_____)	_____
TOTAL	–$ _____

Do you have any outstanding loans or lines of credit?

LENDERS	OUTSTANDING AMOUNT	INTEREST RATE (%)
_____	_____	_____
_____	_____	_____
_____	_____	_____
_____	_____	_____
_____	_____	_____
TOTAL	–$ _____	

Now it's time to calculate your net worth:

First, add up all your assets and record that number here:

Total assets: +$ _____

Then add up your liabilities and record that number here:

Total liabilities: – _____

Now, subtract your total liabilities from your total assets to arrive at your net worth:

+/–$ _____

Now list your liabilities from highest interest rate to lowest. Don't be surprised if your credit card debt ranks highest—department store cards are usually the worst.

LIABILITY	INTEREST RATE (%)
1. _____	_____
2. _____	_____
3. _____	_____
4. _____	_____
5. Other (_____)	_____

This listing reflects the order in which you'll want to pay off your debt: The higher the interest rate, the sooner you'll want to retire the debt. Perhaps you can negotiate a loan from your bank to consolidate your debts at a lower interest rate. Or try to pay off your debt with your savings. Although you will lessen your savings, the interest on the savings is likely far less than the interest your debt accrues. Also look into credit cards that offer lower interest rates. Your debit card, which is linked directly to your bank account, may be a better choice for you than a credit card, as it only allows you to use money you actually have.

Cash Flow

Now let's look at your cash flow: what comes in on a regular basis and what goes out. Analyzing it will help you determine in which areas you have control. The more detailed you are here, the better. If you're at all like me, you will be surprised at how many incidental expenses you have. One of the best ways to understand incidental spending is to keep track for a week of every single thing you pay for, from an expensive dinner out, right down to a meter parking fee or subway token. It's not fun, but the results are telling and will let you better control your spending.

First, let's look at your fixed costs. Some items, such as home repairs, food, and gas, you may need to estimate.

Fixed Costs	Monthly	Yearly
Rent/mortgage payment		
Property tax		
Home maintenance and repairs		
Appliance maintenance and repairs		
Homeowner's and contents insurance		
Car lease or loan		
Gas		
Car insurance		
Car maintenance and repairs		
Telephone, including long distance and internet		
Mobile phone		
Cable or satellite TV		
Electricity and other utilities		
Gas or oil heating		
Food		
Clothing		
Personal care		
Health care		
Education expense		
Children (daycare, toys, child support)		
Charitable donations		
Entertainment and gifts		
Vacation		
Other (_____)		
Other (_____)		
Other (_____)		
TOTAL	–$	–$

Now, how much money comes in every month? If it varies, estimate the average monthly income after taxes and deductions. Also note your annual income.

Monthly income: $ _____

Yearly income: $ _____

To determine whether your cash flow is positive or negative, that is, whether you have a monthly or yearly surplus or deficit, subtract your costs from your gross income:

	MONTHLY	YEARLY
Gross income	$ _____	$ _____
minus taxes	–$ _____	–$ _____
minus fixed costs (taken from calculations above)		
=	+/–$ _____	+/–$ _____

SO, ARE YOUR FINANCES cash flow positive (more comes in than goes out) or cash flow negative? If negative, perhaps the money coming in isn't as high as you need it to be. Or maybe you need to be more aggressive in lowering your discretionary spending. Take a minute now to put a star next to those items for which you have a choice how much to spend, as opposed to those that are not discretionary costs. Add up the non-discretionary costs, then the discretionary ones. Do you see areas where you might reduce costs? For example, look into various payment plans for your mobile phone to see which is the best, and ask yourself if you really need all the television stations you've ordered. Small changes add up to a big difference over the year. Review your cash flow once you try to reduce certain items you can control. Then ask yourself:

Do you think your income is enough to cover your fixed costs and to save some money every month as well?   ☐ Yes   ☐ No

If the answer is yes, realistically how much can you save each month?

$ _____

It's prudent to save around 10 percent or more of your annual income. This will assist you should you change jobs or be faced with an unforeseen situation that costs money. It will also work toward your retirement goals (more on that below). It's also ideal to have at least 6 months' income or living expenses put away for emergencies.

This next question will help you plan for future large costs.

When will you next be making a major expenditure? About how much will it cost?

ITEM	YEAR	COST ESTIMATE
Children's education (list names below)		
1. _____	_____	_____
2. _____	_____	_____
3. _____	_____	_____
4. _____	_____	_____
Car	_____	_____
Roof	_____	_____
Furnace	_____	_____
Home renovations	_____	_____
Holiday/travel	_____	_____
Other (_____)	_____	_____
Other (_____)	_____	_____

Seeing the cost estimate of these expenditures in black and white and in relation to the other financial information you've recorded here should give you a sense of how big an expenditure it is and how it will affect your financial health. Some of these expenditures will of course be discretionary. Even so, they may create the need to make changes to your financial situation.

Keeping a money journal will help you in analyzing and solving some of your financial woes. (I've included a sample money journal at the end of this chapter, on page 160.) To save more of your income, you need to have an accounting of where you spend. I compare a money journal to a food journal in which you record everything you eat in a day so you understand where and why you are over- (or under-) eating. It can be tedious, but the results are always telling. Keeping a money journal is especially prudent if you aren't saving enough to meet your financial goals, if you feel your spending is out of control, or if you're expecting a change in your life that will affect your financial situation. Keep a money journal for 6 months, at the end of each month taking a look to see where you can make positive adjustments.

Career Changes

I'm one who believes that if you're not happy at your workplace, it's difficult to be happy outside work and to lead a balanced life. Yet so many of us feel stuck in our jobs. Even if the job is well suited to our expertise, pays well, and offers a good benefits package, we still may not feel satisfied or fulfilled. If going to work each day is a chore, it may be time to consider changing jobs.

I have changed careers a few times. I was fortunate that my husband's income allowed me this flexibility. I started out as a junior high teacher, then I went back to university to complete two post-graduate degrees, then I embarked on my career of writing cookbooks. It was this field that seemed to make me feel the most satisfied, and it has branched out into catering, public speaking, and in general being an authority on healthy living—all while raising four children. I now earn a living at this career that evolved over time.

Of course, many people do not have the financial luxury of simply leaving their jobs. But you can plan toward making a career change if you secure your financial situation and start saving so that you have 6 months or more of income put away to carry you through while you explore career options.

Start practically by thinking about your interests and talents. First, can your new career choice afford you the living you need or want? If you're considering running your own business, ask yourself whether you have the self-discipline that such a move requires.

You can plan toward making a career change if you secure your financial situation. You'll need 6 months or more of income put away so you can explore your options.

where am I now?

Am I happy and fulfilled in the job/career I have now? ☐ Yes ☐ No

Am I satisfied with my income level in my current job? ☐ Yes ☐ No

Do I enjoy the people I work with? ☐ Yes ☐ No

Do the hours I work allow for a balance in my life? ☐ Yes ☐ No

Is my job challenging enough for my skills? ☐ Yes ☐ No

Is there room for advancement if I wish? ☐ Yes ☐ No

After considering the questions above, you may have decided that you need to re-evaluate your present career. You'll want to incorporate both your realities and your dreams into your career plan.

where do I want to be?

Do I need to start my own business in order to pursue that passion? ☐ Yes ☐ No

If so, can it afford me the lifestyle I now have? ☐ Yes ☐ No

Do I need to think about additional schooling to fulfill my career dream? ☐ Yes ☐ No

If so, can I afford the loss of income and the costs associated with that education? ☐ Yes ☐ No

Instead of starting a business or going back to school, do I need to think of changing jobs or employers to get where I want to go? ☐ Yes ☐ No

Is this a viable option? ☐ Yes ☐ No

If no, what other options are available to me?

_____

_____

_____

What is my passion—what am I most interested in?

_____

_____

_____

Can I make a living in some way pursuing that passion? (Be creative in your thinking.)

_____

_____

_____

Should I consider taking a job with less pay in the short term in order to gain the experience I need to get the job I really want? ☐ Yes ☐ No

What other priorities do I have in my life besides career?

_____

_____

_____

Will my career choice allow the flexibility I need to pursue those priorities? ☐ Yes ☐ No

Making a big career change is not easy. It takes courage, commitment, and time—each in small steps. There are likely many variables and permutations to your answers to these questions. You sometimes have to try on a few different options before you find the one that really fits. But, doing truly fulfilling work is well worth striving for. Most of us spend half our waking hours working; wouldn't you want it to be something you love doing?

If you want to make a change in your career, talk to anyone you can in the field you are interested in. They may be able to give you a knowledgeable opinion as to whether it is indeed a feasible career for you, as well as valuable pointers and advice as to how to get to where you want to be. And network: It's amazing how many opportunities can develop out of people you know. But above all, always be realistic about your ambitions. Understand what's possible and what's not.

As I mentioned above, many financial experts believe that everyone should have a reserve fund of at least 6 months' worth of living expenses. This is especially important if you plan to leave your current job to pursue other career options.

Retirement Plans

Putting money into an RRSP, or registered retirement savings plan, is an effective and simple way to save for your retirement. Several types of investments can be registered, or tax sheltered, within an RRSP—from bonds to mutual funds. You can contribute to your RRSP throughout the year, up to a certain amount (dictated by Canada Revenue Agency). Any profits you earn with that money aren't taxed until you remove the money from the fund—usually at retirement—but are rolled back into the investment, at a compounding rate of interest, thereby increasing your retirement savings. You may also withdraw RRSP funds without including them as part of your income at tax time to put toward the purchase of your first home. Another great benefit is that the amount contributed to your RRSP can be deducted from your income, therefore reducing your taxes owing. Various financial institutions can set up an RRSP for you; just make sure when you're investing that it's an RRSP account, as opposed to a non-registered account, on which you may have to pay taxes annually and which you cannot claim against your income when it comes to tax time.

Resources to Help You

As is probably clear to you by now, the key to getting to where you want to be is financial planning. A number of tools are available to help you reach your goals. Computer software programs, such as Quicken, will help you organize your finances on a monthly and yearly basis. There are also some excellent personal finance books. The old standby, which I really like, is *The*

Wealthy Barber, by Canadian-born David Chilton. I also like *Rich Dad, Poor Dad: What the Rich Teach Their Kids About Money—That the Poor and Middle Class Do Not!* by Robert T. Kiyosaki. Both will provide you with common sense advice. The financial planning books in the Complete Idiot Guide series and also in the Dummies series are well detailed and self-explanatory. What you definitely want to avoid is any book outlining a get-rich-quick scheme: If it seems too good to be true, it probably is.

There are also a number of financial advisors out there hoping to help with your investment strategy. The right financial planner can—

1. Help define your financial problems.
2. Help you set realistic goals with a practical strategy that you can follow and understand. Often just setting priorities will help you feel more balanced in your situation and help in your long-term and future financial decisions.
3. Bridge the gap in your family's financial decisions. More family arguments are over money than anything else. Consider your advisor your financial therapist.
4. Help you earn money in your investments while reaching your short- and long-term goals.

The time you save by consulting with a financial planner will allow you to focus on other areas of your life that need attention. But you need to do your homework before entrusting your hard-earned money to someone else. This doesn't mean there aren't plenty of well-qualified advisors. Ask your friends for recommendations. Associations and financial planning organizations can also refer you to a professional in your area. You want to be confident that you are hiring a competent, financially unbiased, and ethical professional. Ask any advisor you are considering using for several references and make sure to call them.

Beware of those financial planners who take a commission. They're often good salespeople. Your best choice is an advisor who takes a percentage of the assets that are being managed and invested. Be aware though that these advisors may try to direct you to those assets with which they earn the largest income. Similarly, if an advisor works for a bank, he or she is going to sell you the bank's products and services, whether or not they are the most appropriate for your situation. You might opt to hire a financial advisor on an hourly basis to help you make intelligent financial decisions about investments, loans, and retirement packages. Such an advisor, though, won't know your financial situation as thoroughly as a financial planner. The more information and knowledge you have about your finances, the easier it will be to work with a financial professional. Not educating yourself at all is like working in the dark. Really make sure you trust your advisor before you agree to work with him or her.

A good financial advisor will direct you toward the concrete steps you need to take to achieve your objectives. He or she can help you with tax sheltered savings such as RRSPs and can help you determine what proportion of your savings to invest in bonds, stocks, and mutual funds, based on your objectives. A good advisor can also tell you whether your objectives can realistically be achieved with the income and costs you have. You may have to reduce your fixed costs and revisit your retirement objectives if they are currently unattainable. Or you may need to consider increasing your income with a career change in order to achieve your goals.

Tailoring Your Financial Plan

Whatever career and financial plan you arrive at, make sure it's a plan designed especially for you—to suit your particular needs and aspirations. Answering the various questions I've posed above will help you direct your goals in a focused manner. Take a good look at your answers and examine where you can make realistic changes. Those needs and aspirations will change over time and periodically going through this question-and-answer process will help you tailor your financial plan to accommodate those changes. After all, most people have more than one career in their working lives. I know of a woman who went back to law school in her forties, after being at home with her four children for years. She wanted to earn money to help pay for their university education when they were ready for it. And we've all heard of people who've decided to go back to school or start a business after a divorce in order to more easily make ends meet as single parents. Many men and women I know of have made career changes to free up time for parenthood.

When your circumstances, motivation, or priorities shift, revisit your financial plan to make sure it still works for you. What matters to you when you're twenty-five is very different from what you care about at fifty-five—your goals, your risk profile, and your asset base are all different and so too will your financial plan be.

Once you have decided on a plan for your future, reaching your savings goals every month is a very satisfying experience. You can relax about your and your family's future, safe in the knowledge that you've been responsible in planning for it. And when you have found the career that fulfills you, you will not only enjoy your life so much more but chances are you may even make more money than you did in your other job. I believe loving your work—or at least loving what your work provides for the rest of your life—is the only way to be successful at it. The finance element is an essential building block in a balanced life. Without it, the rest of your life can be too easily thrown out of whack.

Reaching your savings goals every month is a very satisfying experience. You can relax about your and your family's future, safe in the knowledge that you've been responsible in planning for it.

A Simple Strategy to Improve Your Finances

What can you do for 30 minutes today to help you improve your financial life? For starters, you can do what many people do at the beginning of a savings program: In a notebook, record every penny you spent today and what it was spent on. If you keep track of your spending this way for a week, you will see your spending pattern. The cappuccino or latte you buy every morning on the way to work for $2.95 adds up to $59 per month and about $700 per year. If you bought an espresso maker, coffee, and milk, you would probably save at least $500 a year. Another area money is spent needlessly is on magazines and newspapers. Subscriptions cost a fraction of the newsstand price. *Vogue* can arrive at your doorstep for $20 per year, as opposed to the $60 you would pay at the store. You can substantially cut your miscellaneous spending in these small ways. And doing so is definitely getting One Thing Right. Be smart with your money and it will last to take care of you in your retirement.

Keeping on Track

Successful spending of your hard-earned money means living within your means. You want to try to get the best value for your money, trim those unnecessary extras, and try to stay out of unnecessary debt, which is often due to uncontrolled spending using credit cards. The more stable your financial situation is, the more balanced the rest of your life will be. Life is change and you need to keep up with the change in terms of your finances. As with your weight, procrastination only deepens the problem. Here are a few tips to keep you on track:

1. Make the You Deserve Financial Health commitment. You work hard in your life. Now commit to taking the steps to ensure your long-term financial well-being. You deserve that kind of peace of mind, and it's essential to the balance of your life.

2. Get out of debt—especially credit card debt, even one small step at a time. Consolidate your debt if possible. If it isn't possible, pay off the debt carrying the highest interest rate first. Either way, make a payment every month until it's gone.

3. Save money for your future. Every month, put a little money aside to take care of your future and invest in retirement plans. Educate yourself about your investment options and then plan realistically for what you'll need to meet your retirement goals—when you will retire and how much money you'll need to do so comfortably.

4. Protect your family. Make sure you have a will and that you have all your estate planning needs addressed. Buy insurance for your life, health, and possessions.

FROM THE PERSPECTIVES of mind, body, and
spirit, by keeping on track with your finances
and your career objectives, you'll challenge your
mind with work you love; you'll eliminate stress
and its detrimental effects on your health by
developing and implementing an effective financial plan; and spiritually, you'll be proud that by
pursuing both you are doing the very best for
you and your family. Love yourself and your
family enough to look after them. It's essential
to the balance of living well.

"Successful spending of your hard-earned
money means living within your means. The
more stable your financial situation is, the
more balanced the rest of your life will be."

my money journal

Spending Areas

Rent

Mortgage

Taxes

Utilities

Food

Car

Transportation

Clothing

Health

Children

Debt

Entertainment

Personal expenses

Education

Insurance

Current Financial Problem

1. e.g., restaurant bills too high

2.

3.

4.

5.

Monthly Expense	% of Total Income

Possible Solution	Action Taken
limit eating out to twice weekly	eat out once at higher-priced restaurant and once at inexpensive take-out

25 favourite recipes getting started on eating right

Minestrone with Diced Chicken and Barley

This soup is a meal in itself. There's nothing quite like a hearty minestrone. The barley in this one gives it a twist. I always flour chicken breasts before sautéing them to retain the moisture. The whole canned tomatoes give more texture and flavour than crushed tomatoes. Just remember to break them down with the back of a wooden spoon occasionally during cooking.

MAKES 8 SERVINGS. NUTRITIONAL ANALYSIS PER SERVING 185 CALORIES, 14 G PROTEIN, 4.1 G FAT, TOTAL, 1.2 G FAT, SATURATED, 18 G CARBOHYDRATES, 257 MG SODIUM, 21 MG CHOLESTEROL, 4.8 G FIBRE

4 oz skinless, boneless chicken breast, diced

1 tbsp all-purpose flour

2 tsp vegetable oil

2 tsp minced garlic

1 cup chopped onions

1 cup chopped carrot

4 1/2 cups beef or chicken stock

1/4 cup pearl barley

1 can (19 oz) whole tomatoes, with juice

1 cup canned chickpeas, drained and rinsed

2 tbsp tomato paste

1 1/2 tsp dried basil

1/2 tsp dried oregano

2 bay leaves

2 cups sliced bok choy

GARNISH

3 tbsp grated Parmesan cheese

1. Dust the chicken with the flour. In a large hot saucepan sprayed with vegetable spray, add the chicken and sauté just until browned, about 4 minutes. Remove the chicken from the saucepan and set aside.

2. In the same saucepan, re-spray with vegetable oil; heat the oil and then add the garlic, onions, and carrots and cook for 5 minutes or until the onions and carrots are softened.

3. Add the stock, barley, tomatoes and juice, chickpeas, tomato paste, basil, oregano, and bay leaves. Cover and simmer for 35 minutes or just until the barley is tender. Stir occasionally, breaking down the tomatoes with the back of a wooden spoon. Add the chicken and bok choy and cook for 2 minutes, just until the bok choy is wilted and the chicken is cooked through. Garnish with Parmesan.

Yellow Split Pea Soup

If you're tired of green split pea soup, this yellow split pea version will be welcome. The peas are full of fibre and complex carbohydrates. The potatoes give the soup its creaminess.

MAKES 6 SERVINGS. NUTRITIONAL ANALYSIS PER SERVING 200 CALORIES, 14 G PROTEIN, 4.1 G FAT, TOTAL, 0.7 G FAT, SATURATED, 40 G CARBOHYDRATES, 480 MG SODIUM, 0 MG CHOLESTEROL, 9.1 G FIBRE

2 tsp vegetable oil

2 tsp minced garlic

1 cup chopped onions

1 cup chopped carrots

1 cup chopped celery

5 cups chicken or vegetable stock

1 cup dried yellow split peas

1 cup diced peeled potatoes

1/8 tsp each salt and pepper

GARNISH

1/4 cup chopped green onions

1/4 cup low-fat plain yogourt
  (optional)

1. In a non-stick saucepan sprayed with vegetable spray, heat oil over medium-high heat; cook garlic, onions, carrots, and celery for 5 minutes or until vegetables are softened and starting to brown. Stir in stock, split peas, potatoes, salt, and pepper. Bring to a boil. Reduce heat to medium-low, cover, and cook for 30 to 35 minutes or until split peas are tender.

2. In batches, purée soup in a blender or food processor. Serve soup sprinkled with green onions and a dollop of yogourt.

Spinach Salad with Candied Pecans, Pears, and Brie

This is the number one salad of my catering company. You'll never tire of eating it. The combination of baby spinach with cinnamon-sugared pecans, ripe pears, and small morsels of brie is sensational, and the dressing uses very little oil, so it is low in fat too. Add some cooked chicken or seafood to the salad and you've got a complete meal.

MAKES 8 SERVINGS. NUTRITIONAL ANALYSIS PER SERVING 189 CALORIES, 4.2 G PROTEIN, 12 G FAT, TOTAL, 2.7 G FAT, SATURATED, 13 G CARBOHYDRATES, 105 MG SODIUM, 9 MG CHOLESTEROL, 2.6 G FIBRE

CANDIED PECANS

1/3 cup pecan halves

3 tbsp icing sugar

1/4 tsp cinnamon

1/8 tsp allspice

1/8 tsp nutmeg

SALAD

8 cups baby spinach

1 cup diced radicchio

1 large ripe pear, peeled, cored, and diced

2 oz brie, diced

DRESSING

2 tbsp orange juice concentrate

2 tbsp olive oil

1 tbsp balsamic vinegar

1 tsp minced garlic

1/2 tsp liquid honey

1/2 tsp Dijon mustard

Preheat oven or toaster oven to 350°F. Spray baking sheet or toaster oven pan with vegetable spray.

1. To make candied pecans: Rinse the pecans with cold water. Drain, but do not let dry. In a small bowl, combine the icing sugar, cinnamon, allspice, and nutmeg. Dip the pecans in this mixture to coat well. Spread on the prepared baking sheet. Bake for 15 minutes. Cool and chop.

2. **To make salad:** In a large bowl, combine the spinach, radicchio, pear, and brie.

3. **To make dressing:** In a small bowl, whisk together orange juice concentrate, oil, vinegar, garlic, honey, and mustard. Pour over the salad and toss to coat. Garnish with the candied pecans.

Grilled Chicken Caesar Salad

Consider this: A plate of not-so-innocent traditional Caesar salad can contain over 500 calories and 30 grams of fat. The high number of calories is because of the oil, cheese, and eggs. My version is delicious yet low in fat and calories. You don't need your salad to be swimming in dressing—there is just enough here. The large Italian croutons make this salad stand out.

MAKES 6 SERVINGS. NUTRITIONAL ANALYSIS PER SERVING 164 CALORIES, 14 G PROTEIN, 7.6 G FAT, TOTAL, 1.8 G FAT, SATURATED, 9.8 G CARBOHYDRATES, 239 MG SODIUM, 61 MG CHOLESTEROL, 1.4 G FIBRE

8 oz boneless chicken breast

2 cups 1-inch Italian bread cubes

DRESSING

1 egg

3 tbsp grated Parmesan cheese

3 anchovy fillets, minced

1 tbsp fresh lemon juice

1 1/2 tsp minced garlic

1 tsp Dijon mustard

1/8 tsp freshly ground pepper

2 tbsp olive oil

6 cups torn romaine lettuce

Preheat oven to 425°F.

1. On grill or non-stick grill pan sprayed with vegetable spray, cook chicken over medium-high heat for 6 minutes per side, or until cooked through. Cut into strips.

2. Place bread cubes on baking sheet. Spray with vegetable spray. Bake for 8 to 10 minutes or until golden, turning once.

3. To make dressing: In a small food processor, or in a bowl using a whisk, beat egg, Parmesan, anchovies, lemon juice, garlic, mustard, and pepper until smooth. Slowly add the olive oil, mixing until thickened.

4. In a bowl, toss together chicken, croutons, and romaine. Pour dressing over; toss to coat.

Greek Feta Burgers

Just by adding some mushrooms, feta cheese, and oregano you have an exciting new burger. I love to serve these on a bed of couscous, forgetting the bun altogether.

MAKES 5 SERVINGS. NUTRITIONAL ANALYSIS PER SERVING 194 CALORIES, 21 G PROTEIN, 9.6 G FAT, TOTAL, 3.6 G FAT, SATURATED, 5.9 G CARBOHYDRATES, 210 MG SODIUM, 76 MG CHOLESTEROL, 0.8 G FIBRE

1 cup chopped mushrooms

1/2 cup chopped onions

2 oz light feta cheese, crumbled

1 lb lean ground beef or lamb

1/4 cup finely chopped fresh chives
   or green onions

3 tbsp chopped fresh oregano
   (or 1 tsp dried)

3 tbsp dried seasoned bread
   crumbs (store-bought)

2 tbsp barbecue sauce

2 tsp minced garlic

1 egg

1. In a non-stick skillet sprayed with vegetable spray, cook mushrooms and onions over medium-high heat for 4 minutes or until softened and browned. Remove from heat. Stir in feta.

2. In a bowl, stir together beef, chives, oregano, bread crumbs, barbecue sauce, garlic, and egg. Stir in onion mixture. Form into 5 patties.

3. Preheat barbecue. On grill sprayed with vegetable spray, cook patties over medium-high heat for 3 to 5 minutes per side or until cooked through. (Or cook in a non-stick grill pan over medium-high heat, turning once; or place on baking sheet and bake in centre of preheated 450°F oven for 10 to 15 minutes or until cooked through, turning once.)

Tex Mex Flank Steak with Corn Salsa

Flank steak is one of my favourite cuts of beef because it is tender and extremely low in fat. With only 4 grams of fat per 3-ounce serving, it has less than half the fat of other cuts of beef—almost the same as white chicken meat. The only caveats are that you must marinate flank steak for at least 2 hours for it to be tender, and you must cut it against the grain or the meat will be stringy.

MAKES 6 SERVINGS. NUTRITIONAL ANALYSIS PER SERVING 226 CALORIES, 24 G PROTEIN, 9.6 G FAT, TOTAL, 3.9 G FAT, SATURATED, 11 G CARBOHYDRATES, 416 MG SODIUM, 59 MG CHOLESTEROL, 0.5 G FIBRE

1 cup barbecue sauce
1/3 cup cider vinegar
2 tbsp molasses
1/4 tsp hot pepper sauce
1 1/2 lb flank steak

CORN SALSA (OPTIONAL)
1 cup canned corn niblets, drained
1 cup diced red bell pepper
1 cup canned black beans, drained
  and rinsed
1/3 cup chopped green onions
1/4 cup chopped coriander

1. In a bowl, whisk together barbecue sauce, vinegar, molasses, and hot pepper sauce. Place flank steak in a shallow glass baking dish. Pour sauce over steak. Cover with plastic wrap. Refrigerate for 2 hours or overnight.

2. To make salsa: In a non-stick skillet sprayed with vegetable spray, sauté corn and bell pepper for 5 minutes or until corn begins to brown. Add beans, onions, and coriander. Set aside.

3. Remove steak from marinade, reserving marinade.

4. Preheat barbecue. On grill sprayed with vegetable spray, cook beef over medium-high heat for 5 to 8 minutes per side or until desired doneness. (Or cook in a non-stick grill pan over medium-high heat.)

5. In a small saucepan, bring reserved marinade to a boil; boil for 5 minutes. Serve steak with sauce and salsa, if desired.

Hoisin Garlic Meatloaf with Oyster Mushroom and Bell Peppers

The weekend meatloaf may be a meal of the past, but this trendy rolled meatloaf will revive the tradition. Be sure to let it cool slightly before slicing. The spiral design exposes the delicious filling.

MAKES 8 SERVINGS. NUTRITIONAL ANALYSIS PER SERVING 248 CALORIES, 19 G PROTEIN, 12 G FAT, TOTAL, 3.6 G FAT, SATURATED, 13 G CARBOHYDRATES, 429 MG SODIUM, 63 MG CHOLESTEROL, 2.3 G FIBRE

FILLING

2 tsp vegetable oil

1/2 cup chopped onions

1 cup chopped oyster mushrooms

1/2 cup chopped red bell pepper

1 tbsp low-sodium soy sauce

1 tbsp hoisin sauce

1 tbsp water

2 tsp finely chopped garlic

2 tsp minced fresh ginger

2 tsp sesame oil

2 tsp rice wine vinegar

MEATLOAF

1 lb extra-lean ground beef

1/4 cup dried seasoned bread crumbs (store-bought)

1/4 cup chopped green onions, whole onion

3 tbsp chopped fresh cilantro or parsley

2 tbsp hoisin sauce

1 tsp minced fresh ginger

1 tsp minced garlic

1 large egg

GLAZE

2 tbsp water

2 tbsp hoisin sauce

1 tsp sesame oil

Preheat oven to 375°F. Spray an 8 1/2 x 4 1/2-inch loaf pan with vegetable spray.

1. To make filling: In a non-stick skillet sprayed with vegetable spray, heat the oil, then add the onions and sauté for 3 minutes. Add the mushrooms and bell pepper and sauté for 5 minutes. Add the soy sauce, hoisin sauce, water, garlic, ginger, sesame oil, and vinegar, and cook for 1 minute.

2. To make meatloaf: In a bowl, stir together the ground beef, bread crumbs, green onions, cilantro, hoisin sauce, ginger, garlic, and egg. Pat into an approximately 10-inch square on waxed paper.

3. Spread the filling vegetables overtop the meatloaf and roll with the help of the waxed paper. Place in the prepared loaf pan, seam-side down.

4. To make the glaze: In a small bowl, whisk together the water, hoisin sauce, and sesame oil. Pour overtop the meatloaf and bake for 35 minutes or until the meat is done to an internal temperature of about 160°F. Let cool for at least 10 minutes before inverting the pan and slicing.

Boneless Chicken Breast Stuffed with Two Olives and Cheese

The combination of black and green olives is what makes this recipe's flavour so interesting—but feel free to use only one type if you prefer. If you don't want to use fresh jalapeños, use 1/2 teaspoon hot sauce or chili paste instead.

MAKES 4 SERVINGS. NUTRITIONAL ANALYSIS PER SERVING 315 CALORIES, 44 G PROTEIN, 11 G FAT, TOTAL, 2.6 G FAT, SATURATED, 8 G CARBOHYDRATES, 493 MG SODIUM, 104 MG CHOLESTEROL, 1.8 G FIBRE

STUFFING

1/3 cup chopped black olives

1/3 cup chopped green olives

1/3 cup chopped parsley

1/4 cup grated Parmesan cheese

2 tsp olive oil

1 tsp minced jalapeño peppers
 (seeded)

1/2 tsp crushed garlic

1/8 tsp freshly ground black pepper

1 1/2 lb skinless, boneless chicken
 breasts (4 single breasts)

3 tbsp all-purpose flour

2 tsp vegetable oil

3/4 cup tomato sauce

1/2 tsp dried basil

GARNISH

1/4 cup chopped basil or parsley

1. To make stuffing: In the bowl of a small food processor, or by hand with a chef's knife, finely mince the olives, parsley, Parmesan, oil, jalapeños, garlic, and black pepper. Make a 2-inch horizontal slit through the thickest end of the breast to form a pocket. Divide the stuffing among the breasts and then dust the breasts with flour. Hold together with a toothpick if desired.

2. Preheat oven to 400°F. Spray a baking pan with vegetable spray.

3. In a hot non-stick skillet sprayed with vegetable spray, add the oil and sauté the breasts on all sides, just until browned, about 5 minutes.

4. Combine the tomato sauce and basil and pour half into the prepared baking pan. Place the chicken on top, pour the remaining sauce overtop, and bake for 15 to 20 minutes or just until the chicken is no longer pink and the internal temperature reaches 170°F. Do not overcook. Garnish with basil or parsley.

Chicken Parmesan with Sun-Dried Tomatoes

The combination of sun-dried tomatoes with sweet bell peppers and tomato sauce is delicious over chicken breasts. I buy sun-dried tomatoes in bulk and use as needed. Just pour boiling water over them and let sit for 15 minutes to rehydrate them. Drain and then chop.

MAKES 4 SERVINGS. NUTRITIONAL ANALYSIS PER SERVING 391 CALORIES, 38 G PROTEIN, 11 G FAT, TOTAL, 2.9 G FAT, SATURATED, 35 G CARBOHYDRATES, 440 MG SODIUM, 127 MG CHOLESTEROL, 4.8 G FIBRE

4 tsp vegetable oil

1 cup chopped onions

1 tsp minced garlic

1 cup chopped red or green bell peppers

1/3 cup chopped rehydrated sun-dried tomatoes

1 cup tomato pasta sauce

1/2 cup chicken stock

1 tsp dried basil

1/2 tsp dried oregano

4 skinless, boneless chicken breasts (about 1 lb.)

1 egg

2 tbsp water

3/4 cup dried seasoned bread crumbs (store-bought)

1 tbsp grated Parmesan cheese

TOPPING

1/3 cup shredded light mozzarella cheese

1 tbsp grated Parmesan cheese

GARNISH

3 tbsp chopped fresh parsley

Preheat oven to 400°F.

1. In a non-stick saucepan sprayed with vegetable spray, heat 2 tsp of the oil over medium heat; cook onions and garlic for 5 minutes or until softened. Stir in peppers and sun-dried tomatoes and cook for 3 minutes. Stir in tomato sauce, chicken stock, basil, and oregano. Bring to a boil. Reduce heat to a simmer; cook, uncovered, for 10 minutes or until thickened.

2. Meanwhile, between 2 sheets of waxed paper, pound chicken breasts to an even 1/2-inch thickness. In a shallow bowl, whisk egg with water. On a separate plate, stir together bread crumbs and 1 tbsp Parmesan.

3. In a large non-stick skillet sprayed with vegetable spray, heat remaining oil over medium-high heat. Dip each chicken breast in the egg mixture; coat each with the bread crumb mixture. Cook for 5 minutes, turning once, or until golden on both sides.

4. Place half of sauce in a 9-inch casserole dish; place chicken on top. Spoon remaining sauce over top. Sprinkle with mozzarella and 1 tbsp Parmesan. Bake, uncovered, for 10 minutes or until chicken is cooked through and cheese is melted. Sprinkle with parsley.

Pesto Stuffed Chicken Rolls

Stuffing and rolling boneless chicken breasts creates an elegant and simple dish, one I frequently serve when entertaining. Serve the chicken rolls whole, cut in half, or sliced into medallions.

MAKES 4 SERVINGS. NUTRITIONAL ANALYSIS PER SERVING 242 CALORIES, 31 G PROTEIN, 7.8 G FAT, TOTAL, 1.9 G FAT, SATURATED, 12 G CARBOHYDRATES, 569 MG SODIUM, 123 MG CHOLESTEROL, 0.8 G FIBRE

4 skinless, boneless chicken breasts (about 1 lb)

1 oz light cream cheese, softened

1 tbsp store-bought or homemade pesto

2 tbsp chopped, roasted red peppers

1 egg

2 tbsp water or low-fat milk

1/2 cup dried seasoned bread crumbs (store-bought)

2 tsp vegetable oil

Preheat oven to 425°F.

1. Between two sheets of waxed paper, pound chicken breasts to an even 1/2-inch thickness.

2. In a small bowl, stir cream cheese and pesto together until smooth. Divide among chicken breasts, spreading thinly over surface. Sprinkle with red peppers. Starting at short end, roll up chicken breasts. Secure edges with toothpicks or small skewers.

3. In a shallow bowl, beat egg with water. Place bread crumbs on a plate.

4. In a large non-stick skillet sprayed with vegetable spray, heat oil over medium-high heat. Dip each chicken roll in egg mixture, then coat in bread crumbs. Cook, turning occasionally, for 3 minutes, or until well browned on all sides. Transfer to a baking sheet sprayed with vegetable spray.

5. Bake for 12 to 14 minutes or until chicken is cooked through. Remove toothpicks before serving.

Salmon Teriyaki

This is one of the earlier recipes I developed. Here I've improved on it, making the sauce more like a glaze. The glaze is tasty on chicken as well.

MAKES 4 SERVINGS. NUTRITIONAL ANALYSIS PER SERVING 250 CALORIES, 24 G PROTEIN, 10 G FAT, TOTAL, 1.6 G FAT, SATURATED, 16 G CARBOHYDRATES, 323 MG SODIUM, 64 MG CHOLESTEROL, 0.3 G FIBRE

1/4 cup packed brown sugar

2 tbsp low-sodium soy sauce

2 tbsp rice wine vinegar

1 tbsp water

2 tsp cornstarch

2 tsp minced garlic

2 tsp sesame oil

1 1/2 tsp minced fresh ginger

4 4-oz skin-on salmon fillets

2 tsp sesame seeds

Preheat oven to 425°F.

1. In a small saucepan, whisk together brown sugar, soy sauce, vinegar, water, cornstarch, garlic, sesame oil, and ginger. Cook over medium heat until thickened and smooth. Remove from heat.

2. Place salmon, skin-side down, on a rimmed baking sheet. Spoon half of sauce over salmon. Sprinkle with sesame seeds. Bake in centre of oven for 10 minutes per inch thickness of fish, or until fish flakes easily when prodded with a fork.

3. Remove fish skin before serving. Serve with remaining sauce on the side.

Tilapia with Tomato, Olive, and Cheese Topping

You can use any firm white fish with this scrumptious olive, tomato, and cheese topping. Tilapia is both delicious and affordable.

MAKES 4 SERVINGS. NUTRITIONAL ANALYSIS PER SERVING 198 CALORIES, 27 G PROTEIN, 8.5 G FAT, TOTAL, 3.6 G FAT, SATURATED, 3.3 G CARBOHYDRATES, 255 MG SODIUM, 60 MG CHOLESTEROL, 0.5 G FIBRE

1 cup chopped plum tomatoes

1/2 cup shredded light mozzarella cheese

1/4 cup chopped black olives

1 1/2 oz goat cheese

1 tsp minced garlic

1 tsp dried basil

1 lb tilapia fillets or other firm white fish (halibut, snapper, haddock)

Preheat oven to 425°F.

1. In a bowl, stir together tomatoes, mozzarella, olives, goat cheese, garlic, and basil.

2. Place tilapia on a rimmed baking sheet. Top with tomato mixture. Bake for 10 minutes per inch thickness of fish and topping, or until fish flakes easily when prodded with a fork.

Sole with Charred Corn and Avocado Salsa

Sole is a delicate and inexpensive fish to prepare. The salsa livens up its mild flavour. Sautéing the corn brings out a flavour and texture as if barbecued. The avocado adds a Southwestern note.

MAKES 4 SERVINGS. NUTRITIONAL ANALYSIS PER SERVING 257 CALORIES, 34 G PROTEIN, 9 G FAT, TOTAL, 1.3 G FAT, SATURATED, 7.5 G CARBOHYDRATES, 201 MG SODIUM, 82 MG CHOLESTEROL, 2.1 G FIBRE

CHARRED CORN AND AVOCADO SALSA

2/3 cup canned corn niblets, drained

2/3 cup diced red bell pepper

1/4 cup diced sweet onions

1/3 cup diced ripe avocado

1/4 cup chopped cilantro or parsley

2 tbsp freshly squeezed lemon juice

1 tbsp olive oil

1 tsp crushed garlic

1/2 tsp hot chili sauce or minced jalapeño

2 tsp vegetable oil

1 1/2 lb sole fillets (4)

1. In a hot non-stick skillet sprayed with vegetable spray, sauté the corn for 5 minutes or until browned. Remove from the heat and add the bell pepper, onions, avocado, cilantro, lemon juice, oil, garlic, and chili sauce or jalapeño.

2. In a clean non-stick skillet sprayed with vegetable spray, heat the oil and cook the sole for 3 to 5 minutes on a high heat or just until cooked. Serve with the salsa.

Roasted Vegetables with Maple Syrup and Cinnamon

Whenever I serve these roasted vegetables, with this subtle maple syrup and cinnamon dressing, they disappear before my eyes. These vegetables also taste great a couple of days later—if there are any leftovers, that is. I serve them alongside fish, chicken, or beef, or on their own as a snack.

MAKES 6 SERVINGS. NUTRITIONAL ANALYSIS PER SERVING 189 CALORIES, 12 G PROTEIN, 2.6 G FAT, TOTAL, 0.4 G FAT, SATURATED, 31 G CARBOHYDRATES, 35 MG SODIUM, 0 MG CHOLESTEROL, 6.7 G FIBRE

1 lb unpeeled sweet potatoes, cut in 1-inch thick slices

1 lb butternut squash, peeled and cut in 2-inch cubes

1 red bell pepper, cored and cut in 4 wedges

1 yellow or orange bell pepper, cored and cut in 4 wedges

1 large sweet onion, cut in 8 wedges

DRESSING

1 tbsp olive oil

1 tbsp balsamic vinegar

1 tbsp pure maple syrup

1/2 tsp cinnamon

GARNISH

1/4 cup chopped fresh parsley

1/4 cup chopped green onions, whole onion

Preheat oven to 425°F. Line two baking sheets with aluminum foil, then spray with vegetable spray.

1. Place the sweet potatoes, squash, peppers, and onions in a single layer on the prepared baking sheets. Spray lightly with vegetable spray. Bake in the centre of the oven for about 25 to 30 minutes, turning after 20 minutes or just until browned and tender. If the trays are on separate racks, switch their positions halfway through cooking time. Place in a serving dish.

2. To make dressing: In a small bowl, whisk together the oil, vinegar, maple syrup, and cinnamon. Pour overtop the vegetables. Garnish with parsley and green onions.

Asparagus with Caesar Dressing

Asparagus is always a delicious and elegant vegetable to serve. It is a source of vitamins C and A and iron, and an excellent source of folate. The Caesar dressing is sensational overtop. Try thinly slicing fresh Parmesan, using a cheese slicer or sharp knife, to use as a garnish.

MAKES 4 SERVINGS. NUTRITIONAL ANALYSIS PER SERVING 76 CALORIES, 4.1 G PROTEIN, 4.4 G FAT, TOTAL, 0.9 G FAT, SATURATED, 5.0 G CARBOHYDRATES, 130 MG SODIUM, 2.9 MG CHOLESTEROL, 1.7 G FIBRE

1 lb asparagus, trimmed

1 tbsp grated Parmesan cheese

1 tbsp olive oil

2 tsp fresh lemon juice

2 tsp water

2 anchovy fillets, chopped

1 tsp crushed garlic

1/2 tsp Dijon mustard

1. Steam or microwave asparagus until tender. Place on a serving dish.

2. In a small bowl, mix 1/2 tbsp of the Parmesan, the olive oil, lemon juice, water, anchovies, garlic, and mustard. Pour over asparagus.

3. Sprinkle with the remaining 1/2 tbsp Parmesan.

Potato Wedge Fries

These will be the best and healthiest french fries you'll ever eat. Experiment, using any seasonings you like. A potato is a powerhouse of nutrients. It provides you with vitamin C, potassium, magnesium, iron, and fibre if eaten with the skin.

MAKES 6 SERVINGS. NUTRITIONAL ANALYSIS PER SERVING 156 CALORIES, 3.0 G PROTEIN, 5.3 G FAT, TOTAL, 1.0 G FAT, SATURATED, 24 G CARBOHYDRATES, 47 MG SODIUM, 1.6 MG CHOLESTEROL, 2.3 G FIBRE

3 large baking potatoes
2 tbsp olive oil
1 tsp minced garlic
2 tbsp grated Parmesan cheese
1/4 tsp chili powder

Preheat oven to 375°F. Spray rimmed baking sheet with vegetable spray.

1. Scrub potatoes and cut lengthwise into 8 wedges. Put on prepared baking sheet.

2. In a small bowl, combine oil and garlic. In another small bowl, combine Parmesan and chili powder. Brush potato wedges with half of oil mixture, then sprinkle with half of Parmesan mixture.

3. Bake for 20 minutes. Turn the wedges; brush with remaining oil mixture and sprinkle with remaining Parmesan mixture. Bake for another 20 minutes or just until potatoes are tender and crisp.

Shoestring Fries

Here's another great recipe using the nutritious potato.

MAKES 4 SERVINGS. NUTRITIONAL ANALYSIS PER SERVING 115 CALORIES, 2.6 G PROTEIN, 4.1 G FAT, TOTAL, 0.8 G FAT, SATURATED, 16.8 G CARBOHYDRATES, 108 MG SODIUM, 1 MG CHOLESTEROL, 1.5 G FIBRE

2 large baking potatoes (about
   1 1/2 lb), unpeeled and scrubbed
2 tbsp grated Parmesan cheese
1 tbsp olive oil
1/8 tsp each salt and freshly ground
   black pepper
1/8 tsp garlic powder
1/8 tsp chili powder

Preheat oven to 425°F. Spray two small rimmed baking sheets with vegetable spray.

1. Cut potatoes lengthwise in half. Slice each half into 8 wedges. Stack and thinly slice wedges into shoestring shapes about 1/4-inch wide. Place in bowl. Add olive oil, Parmesan, salt, pepper, garlic powder, and chili powder and toss well. Spread out on baking sheets.

2. Bake in centre of oven for 40 to 45 minutes, turning fries occasionally, until browned and crisp.

Garlic Mashed Potatoes with Caramelized Onions

Here's a great variation on mashed potatoes. The caramelized onions mixed into the potato and served overtop make this dish a winner. I love the potatoes with meat, chicken, or just by themselves.

MAKES 6 SERVINGS. NUTRITIONAL ANALYSIS PER SERVING 142 CALORIES, 4.2 G PROTEIN, 3.4 G FAT, TOTAL, 1 G FAT, SATURATED, 23.6 G CARBOHYDRATES, 112 MG SODIUM, 3 MG CHOLESTEROL, 3.9 G FIBRE

GARLIC MASHED POTATOES

2 medium Yukon Gold potatoes
    (about 1 lb), peeled and cubed
1/3 cup low-fat sour cream
1 tbsp olive oil
2 tsp minced garlic
1/4 tsp each salt and freshly ground
    black pepper

CARAMELIZED ONIONS

6 cups sliced sweet onions
    (about 2 large)
1 tbsp minced garlic
1 tbsp balsamic vinegar
2 tsp packed brown sugar

GARNISH

2 tbsp chopped fresh parsley

1. To make potatoes: Place potatoes in a saucepan; add cold water to cover. Bring to a boil; cook for 15 to 20 minutes or until tender when pierced with the tip of a sharp knife. Drain potatoes; mash. Stir in sour cream, olive oil, garlic, salt, and pepper. Set potatoes aside.

2. To make onions: Meanwhile, in a large non-stick skillet sprayed with vegetable spray and set over medium-high heat, cook onions for 10 minutes or until they begin to brown and soften, stirring occasionally. Reduce heat to low; add the garlic, vinegar, and brown sugar. Cook for 15 to 20 minutes, stirring occasionally, until onions turn brown.

3. Stir half of the onion mixture into the potatoes; place in a serving dish. Scatter remaining onion mixture overtop. Serve sprinkled with parsley.

Couscous, Chickpea, and Cranberry Salad

This is a beautiful couscous salad. I love to serve it as part of a buffet meal. The sweet orange dressing goes so well with the dried cranberries, chickpeas, and basil.

MAKES 6 SERVINGS. NUTRITIONAL ANALYSIS PER SERVING 235 CALORIES, 6.2 G PROTEIN, 3.2 G FAT, TOTAL, 0.7 G FAT, SATURATED, 45 G CARBOHYDRATES, 204 MG SODIUM, 0 MG CHOLESTEROL, 3.7 G FIBRE

1 cup chicken stock

1 cup couscous

1/2 tsp curry powder (optional)

3/4 cup canned chickpeas, rinsed and drained

1/3 cup dried cranberries

1/4 cup chopped green onions

1/4 cup diced red bell pepper

1/4 cup chopped fresh basil

DRESSING

1 tbsp olive oil

2 tbsp thawed orange juice concentrate

2 tbsp fresh lemon juice

2 tsp grated orange rind

3 tbsp liquid honey

1 tsp minced garlic

1. In a small saucepan, bring stock to a boil. Remove from heat. Stir in couscous and curry powder; cover and let stand for 5 minutes. Fluff with a fork. Transfer to a large bowl and cool.

2. Stir chickpeas, cranberries, green onions, bell pepper, and basil into cooled couscous.

3. To make dressing: In a small bowl, whisk together olive oil, orange juice concentrate, lemon juice, orange rind, honey, and garlic. Pour over couscous mixture; toss to coat.

Chicken and Hoisin Fried Rice

My kids say this is better than any fried rice they've eaten in a Chinese restaurant. Traditional fried rice is often made with lard or excess amounts of oil, adding greatly to the fat and calorie content. This version calls for only 1 tablespoon of vegetable oil, and the hoisin sauce adds moisture. You could also substitute cooked beef, pork, shrimp, or firm tofu for the chicken. I freeze remainders of this rice in small containers for the kids' lunches the next day. Add other vegetables of your choice.

MAKES 4 SERVINGS. NUTRITIONAL ANALYSIS PER SERVING 254 CALORIES, 18 G PROTEIN, 5.1 G FAT, TOTAL, 0.6 G FAT, SATURATED, 34 G CARBOHYDRATES, 708 MG SODIUM, 33 MG CHOLESTEROL, 3.1 G FIBRE

1 cup long-grain rice

8 oz skinless, boneless chicken breast

1/3 cup chicken stock

3 tbsp low-sodium soy sauce

3 tbsp hoisin sauce

2/3 cup chopped carrots

1 tbsp vegetable oil

1 cup chopped red bell pepper

1 cup chopped snow peas

1 1/2 tsp minced garlic

1 tsp minced fresh ginger

GARNISH

2 green onions, chopped

1. In a saucepan, bring 1 1/4 cups water to a boil. Stir in rice. Cover; reduce heat to low and cook for 12 minutes. Remove from heat. Let stand, covered, for 10 minutes. Transfer to bowl. Cool.

2. Preheat barbecue. On grill sprayed with vegetable spray, cook chicken over medium-high heat for 6 minutes per side or until cooked through. (Or cook in a non-stick grill pan over medium-high heat for 12 minutes, turning once, or until cooked through.) Dice.

3. In a small bowl, whisk together stock, soy sauce, and hoisin sauce. Set aside.

4. In a pot of boiling water, cook carrots for 4 minutes or until tender crisp. Drain.

5. In a non-stick wok or large skillet, sprayed with vegetable spray, heat oil over high heat; cook bell pepper, snow peas, garlic, fresh ginger, and the carrots for 2 minutes, stirring constantly. Add rice; cook, stirring, for 2 minutes longer. Add stock mixture and chicken; cook for 1 minute longer or until heated through. Serve garnished with green onions.

Wild Rice and Brown Rice Pilaf with Dried Fruit and Pecans

This is one of my favourite rice dishes. Both the wild and brown rice can be cooked together, and they blend well with the dried fruits. Very little oil is needed because of all the flavours in the salad. I serve this dish as a side salad to my meals or as a buffet item.

MAKES 8 SERVINGS. NUTRITIONAL ANALYSIS PER SERVING 258 CALORIES, 6.4 G PROTEIN, 9.5 G FAT, TOTAL, 1.4 G FAT, SATURATED, 33 G CARBOHYDRATES, 107 MG SODIUM, 1.9 MG CHOLESTEROL, 3.5 G FIBRE

3/4 cup wild rice

3/4 cup brown rice

4 cups vegetable or chicken stock

1/2 cup chopped toasted pecans

1/2 cup chopped green onions, whole onion

1/2 cup dried cranberries

1/2 cup dried chopped apricots

1/2 cup chopped fresh cilantro or parsley

DRESSING

1 tbsp olive oil

1 tbsp thawed orange juice concentrate

1 tbsp freshly squeezed lemon juice

2 tsp low-sodium soy sauce

2 tsp raspberry or balsamic vinegar

1 1/2 tsp sesame oil

1 tsp minced garlic

1. In a saucepan, combine both types of rice with the stock. Bring to a boil. Reduce heat to a simmer, cover and cook for 35 to 40 minutes or just until the rice is tender. Drain excess liquid. Place in a large bowl. Cool.

2. Stir the pecans, green onions, cranberries, apricots, and cilantro into the cooled rice.

3. To make dressing: In a small bowl, whisk together the olive oil, orange juice concentrate, lemon juice, soy sauce, vinegar, sesame oil, and garlic. Pour over the rice mixture and toss to coat.

Rose's Lower-Fat Philadelphia Cheese Steak

Philly steaks—grilled thin steak topped with loads of cooked vegetables and cheese—are all the rage now in Canada. As the name makes clear, this dish originated in Philadelphia. I've adapted this recipe from that of a great new restaurant called Steak Escape, using a thicker steak and more delicious caramelized vegetables.

MAKES 8 HALF SANDWICH SERVINGS. NUTRITIONAL ANALYSIS PER SERVING 170 CALORIES, 12 G PROTEIN, 8.2 G FAT, TOTAL, 3.4 G FAT, SATURATED, 9 G CARBOHYDRATES, 129 MG SODIUM, 28 MG CHOLESTEROL, 2.2 G FIBRE

2 tsp vegetable oil

2 cups sliced onions

2 tsp crushed garlic

2 tsp brown sugar

1/8 tsp salt

1/8 tsp freshly ground black pepper

1 cup sliced red bell pepper

1 cup sliced green bell pepper

8 oz grilling steak

3 tbsp low-fat sour cream

2 tbsp low-fat mayonnaise

2 tsp prepared grated horseradish

2 oz (3/4 cup) grated provolone or
    Gruyère cheese

4 small whole-wheat rolls (6-inch)

Preheat oven to 425°F. Line a baking sheet with aluminum foil.

1. In a large non-stick skillet sprayed with vegetable spray, heat the oil, then add the onions. Sauté for 8 minutes on medium heat. Add the garlic, brown sugar, salt, pepper, and then the bell peppers. Sauté for another 5 minutes. Keep warm.

2. In a hot non-stick grill or skillet sprayed with vegetable spray, cook the steak just until done to your preference. Cool for 5 minutes, then slice thinly. Add to the vegetable mixture.

3. Combine the sour cream, mayonnaise, and horseradish. Spread thinly over both sides of the rolls. Divide the steak and vegetable mixture among 4 rolls, sprinkle with cheese, and replace the top half of the bun. Slice in half. Bake for 5 minutes.

Beef and Sautéed Corn Chili

Sautéing the corn until it is brown gives this chili its distinctive taste. Make it vegetarian by substituting ground soy, found in the produce section of your supermarket, for the beef.

MAKES 6 SERVINGS. NUTRITIONAL ANALYSIS PER SERVING 320 CALORIES, 18 G PROTEIN, 7 G FAT, TOTAL, 2 G FAT, SATURATED, 40 G CARBOHYDRATES, 300 MG SODIUM, 16 MG CHOLESTEROL, 7 G FIBRE

2 tsp vegetable oil

1 1/2 cups chopped onions

1 cup canned corn niblets, drained

2 tsp minced garlic

8 oz extra-lean ground beef

1 can (19 oz) red kidney beans, rinsed and drained

2 1/2 cups tomato pasta sauce

1 cup diced potato

1/2 cup chicken or beef stock

2 tsp chili powder

1 1/2 tsp dried basil

1 tsp brown sugar

1/2 tsp ground cumin

GARNISH

1/4 cup chopped fresh parsley (optional)

1. In a non-stick skillet sprayed with vegetable spray, heat oil over medium heat; cook onions for 5 minutes or until soft. Stir in corn and garlic; cook for 8 minutes or until corn is browned. Stir in beef; cook for 5 minutes or just until beef is cooked.

2. Stir in kidney beans, pasta sauce, potato, stock, chili powder, basil, brown sugar, and cumin. Bring to a boil, reduce heat, and simmer, covered, for 25 to 30 minutes or just until potatoes are soft. Serve sprinkled with parsley.

Triple Chocolate Brownies

I created this recipe for the Mövenpick chain of restaurants in Toronto, which sold more than 1500 of these brownies each month. Now it's the number one dessert at my catering company for corporate Toronto. Not only are these brownies lower in fat than many other versions, but they are totally satisfying.

MAKES 12 SERVINGS. NUTRITIONAL ANALYSIS PER SERVING **40 CALORIES, 2.3 G PROTEIN, 7 G FAT, TOTAL, 1.5 G FAT, SATURATED, 20 G CARBOHYDRATES, 19 MG CHOLESTEROL, 1.2 G FIBRE**

BROWNIES

2/3 cup sugar

1/4 cup vegetable oil

1 egg

1 tsp vanilla

1/3 cup unsweetened cocoa
    powder

1/3 cup all-purpose flour

1 tsp baking powder

1/4 cup low-fat yogourt or sour
    cream

1/4 cup semi-sweet chocolate chips

ICING

2 oz light cream cheese

2/3 cup icing sugar

1 1/2 tsp cocoa powder

1 1/2 tsp water

Preheat oven to 350°F. Spray an 8-inch square metal baking pan with vegetable spray.

1. To make brownies: In a bowl, combine sugar, oil, egg, and vanilla until well mixed. Add cocoa; mix well. Add flour, baking powder, yogourt, and chocolate chips, mixing just until combined and smooth. Don't overmix.

2. Pour batter into prepared pan; bake in centre of oven for 15 to 20 minutes just until set. Do not overbake. Cool.

3. To make icing: In a blender or food processor, blend icing ingredients until smooth. Spread over brownie batch. Cut into squares.

New York–Style Cheesecake

Remember Carnegie Deli New York Cheesecake? The piece that could serve six people? At something like 960 calories and more than 50 grams of fat a slice, it is hard to forget. Here's my much healthier version that's so creamy you'll never believe the calorie count.

MAKES 12 SERVINGS. NUTRITIONAL ANALYSIS PER SERVING 223 CALORIES, 7 G PROTEIN, 7 G FAT, TOTAL, 2.6 G FAT, SATURATED, 33 G CARBOHYDRATES, 31 MG CHOLESTEROL, 0.6 G FIBRE

CRUST

2 cups vanilla wafer or graham cracker crumbs (To make crumbs from vanilla wafers, process them in a food processor until crumbly.)

2 1/2 tbsp water

2 tbsp granulated sugar

1 tbsp vegetable oil

FILLING

1 2/3 cups smooth light ricotta cheese

3 oz light cream cheese, softened

3/4 cup granulated sugar

1/3 cup low-fat plain yogourt

1 egg

1 1/2 tbsp all-purpose flour

2 tsp fresh lemon juice

1 tsp vanilla

GLAZE

2 tbsp strawberry or apple jelly

GARNISH

Berries and/or sliced fresh fruit

Preheat oven to 350°F. Spray an 8-inch springform pan with vegetable spray.

1. To make crust: In a bowl, stir together all crust ingredients until blended. Press onto bottom and partway up side of prepared pan.

2. To make filling: In a food processor or blender, purée all filling ingredients until smooth. Pour into crust.

3. Bake in centre of oven for 35 to 40 minutes or just until centre of cheesecake is still slightly loose. Cool on a wire rack to room temperature. Refrigerate for 2 hours or until chilled.

4. To make glaze: Melt jelly in microwave for 20 seconds. Decorate cheesecake with berries or sliced fruit. Brush glaze overtop.

Index